Glencoe McGraw-Hill

Chapter 8 Resource Masters

Algebra 2

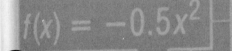

$f(x) = -0.5x^2$

D1228069

McGraw Hill Glencoe

CONSUMABLE WORKBOOKS Many of the worksheets contained in the Chapter Resource Masters booklets are available as consumable workbooks in both English and Spanish.

	ISBN10	ISBN13
Study Guide and Intervention Workbook	0-07-890861-2	978-0-07-890861-3
Homework Practice Workbook	0-07-890862-0	978-0-07-890862-0

Spanish Version

Homework Practice Workbook	0-07-890866-3	978-0-07-890866-8

Answers for Workbooks The answers for Chapter 8 of these workbooks can be found in the back of this Chapter Resource Masters booklet.

StudentWorks Plus™ This CD-ROM includes the entire Student Edition text along with the English workbooks listed above.

TeacherWorks Plus™ All of the materials found in this booklet are included for viewing, printing, and editing in this CD-ROM.

Spanish Assessment Masters (ISBN10: 0-07-890869-8, ISBN13: 978-0-07-890869-9) These masters contain a Spanish version of Chapter 8 Test Form 2A and Form 2C.

The *McGraw-Hill* Companies

 Glencoe

Send all inquiries to:
Glencoe/McGraw-Hill
8787 Orion Place
Columbus, OH 43240

ISBN 13: 978-0-07-890533-9
ISBN 10: 0-07-890533-8

Printed in the United States of America.

1 2 3 4 5 6 7 8 9 10 045 14 13 12 11 10 09 08

Contents

Teacher's Guide to Using the
Chapter 8 Resource Masters

The *Chapter 8 Resource Masters* includes the core materials needed for Chapter 8. These materials include worksheets, extensions, and assessment options. The answers for these pages appear at the back of this booklet.

All of the materials found in this booklet are included for viewing and printing on the *TeacherWorks Plus*™ CD-ROM.

Chapter Resources

Student-Built Glossary (pages 1–2) These masters are a student study tool that presents up to twenty of the key vocabulary terms from the chapter. Students are to record definitions and/or examples for each term. You may suggest that students highlight or star the terms with which they are not familiar. Give this to students before beginning Lesson 8-1. Encourage them to add these pages to their mathematics study notebooks. Remind them to complete the appropriate words as they study each lesson.

Anticipation Guide (pages 3–4) This master, presented in both English and Spanish, is a survey used before beginning the chapter to pinpoint what students may or may not know about the concepts in the chapter. Students will revisit this survey after they complete the chapter to see if their perceptions have changed.

Lesson Resources

Study Guide and Intervention These masters provide vocabulary, key concepts, additional worked-out examples and Check Your Progress exercises to use as a reteaching activity. It can also be used in conjunction with the Student Edition as an instructional tool for students who have been absent.

Skills Practice This master focuses more on the computational nature of the lesson. Use as an additional practice option or as homework for second-day teaching of the lesson.

Practice This master closely follows the types of problems found in the Exercises section of the Student Edition and includes word problems. Use as an additional practice option or as homework for second-day teaching of the lesson.

Word Problem Practice This master includes additional practice in solving word problems that apply the concepts of the lesson. Use as an additional practice or as homework for second-day teaching of the lesson.

Enrichment These activities may extend the concepts of the lesson, offer a historical or multicultural look at the concepts, or widen students' perspectives on the mathematics they are learning. They are written for use with all levels of students.

Graphing Calculator, TI–NSpire Calculator, or Spreadsheet Activities These activities present ways in which technology can be used with the concepts in some lessons of this chapter. Use as an alternative approach to some concepts or as an integral part of your lesson presentation.

Assessment Options

The assessment masters in the *Chapter 8 Resource Masters* offer a wide range of assessment tools for formative (monitoring) assessment and summative (final) assessment.

Student Recording Sheet This master corresponds with the standardized test practice at the end of the chapter.

Extended Response Rubric This master provides information for teachers and students on how to assess performance on open-ended questions.

Quizzes Four free-response quizzes offer assessment at appropriate intervals in the chapter.

Mid-Chapter Test This 1-page test provides an option to assess the first half of the chapter. It parallels the timing of the Mid-Chapter Quiz in the Student Edition and includes both multiple-choice and free-response questions.

Vocabulary Test This test is suitable for all students. It includes a list of vocabulary words and 12 questions to assess students' knowledge of those words. This can also be used in conjunction with one of the leveled chapter tests.

Leveled Chapter Tests

- *Form 1* contains multiple-choice questions and is intended for use with below grade level students.
- *Forms 2A and 2B* contain multiple-choice questions aimed at on grade level students. These tests are similar in format to offer comparable testing situations.
- *Forms 2C and 2D* contain free-response questions aimed at on grade level students. These tests are similar in format to offer comparable testing situations.
- *Form 3* is a free-response test for use with above grade level students.

All of the above mentioned tests include a free-response Bonus question.

Extended-Response Test Performance assessment tasks are suitable for all students. Sample answers and a scoring rubric are included for evaluation.

Standardized Test Practice These three pages are cumulative in nature. It includes three parts: multiple-choice questions with bubble-in answer format, griddable questions with answer grids, and short-answer free-response questions.

Answers

- The answers for the Anticipation Guide and Lesson Resources are provided as reduced pages.
- Full-size answer keys are provided for the assessment masters.

Chapter Resources

8 Student-Built Glossary

This is an alphabetical list of key vocabulary terms you will learn in Chapter 8. As you study this chapter, complete each term's definition or description. Remember to add the page number where you found the term. Add these pages to your Algebra Study Notebook to review vocabulary at the end of the chapter.

Chapter Resources

Vocabulary Term	Found on Page	Definition/Description/Example
asymptote		
Change of Base Formula		
common logarithm LAW·guh·RIH·thuhm		
compound interest		
decay factor		
exponential (EHK·spuh·NEHN·chuhl) decay		
exponential equation		
exponential function		
exponential growth		

(continued on the next page)

8 Student-Built Glossary

Vocabulary Term	Found on Page	Definition/Description/Example
exponential inequality		
growth factor		
logarithm		
logarithmic (LAW·guh·RIHTH·mihk) equation		
logarithmic function		
logarithmic inequality		
natural base, *e*		
natural base exponential function		
natural logarithm		

8 Anticipation Guide

Exponential and Logarithmic Functions and Relations

Step 1 *Before you begin Chapter 8*

- Read each statement.

- Decide whether you Agree (A) or Disagree (D) with the statement.

- Write A or D in the first column OR if you are not sure whether you agree or disagree, write NS (Not Sure).

STEP 1 A, D, or NS	Statement	STEP 2 A or D
	1. The graph of any exponential function is continuous.	
	2. In the exponential function $y = ab^x$, if a is negative then y represents exponential decay.	
	3. If $21^x > 21^3$, then $x > 3$.	
	4. The inverse of $y = b^x$ is $y = \left(\dfrac{1}{b}\right)^x$.	
	5. $3^2 = 9$ in logarithmic form is $\log_2 3 = 9$.	
	6. If $\log_3(2x) = \log_3(x^2 + 1)$, then $2x = x^2 + 1$.	
	7. The logarithm of a product is the product of the logarithms of its factors.	
	8. $4\log_5 9$ is equal to $\log_5 9^4$.	
	9. Common logarithms are logarithms with a base of 2, 5, or 10.	
	10. A natural logarithm is a logarithm with base e.	
	11. Exponential decay is when a quantity decreases by a fixed amount during a certain period of time.	
	12. The percent of increase in an exponential growth problem is called the *rate of growth*.	

Step 2 *After you complete Chapter 8*

- Reread each statement and complete the last column by entering an A or a D.

- Did any of your opinions about the statements change from the first column?

- For those statements that you mark with a D, use a piece of paper to write an example of why you disagree.

8 Ejercicios preparatorios

Relaciones exponenciales y logarítmicas

PASO 1   *Antes de comenzar el Capítulo 8*

- Lee cada enunciado.

- Decide si estás de acuerdo (A) o en desacuerdo (D) con el enunciado.

- Escribe A o D en la primera columna O si no estás seguro(a) de la respuesta, escribe NS (No estoy seguro(a).

PASO 1 A, D o NS	Enunciado	PASO 2 A o D
	1. La gráfica de cualquier función exponencial es continua.	
	2. En la función exponencial $y = ab^x$, si a es negativa, entonces y representa desintegración exponencial.	
	3. Si $21^x > 21^3$, then $x > 3$.	
	4. El inverso de $y = b^x$ es $y = \left(\frac{1}{b}\right)^x$.	
	5. $3^2 = 9$ en forma logarítmica es $\log_2 3 = 9$.	
	6. Si $\log_3(2x) = \log_3(x^2 + 1)$, entonces $2x = x^2 + 1$.	
	7. El logaritmo de un producto es el producto de los logaritmos de sus factores.	
	8. $4\log_5 9$ es igual a $\log_5 9^4$.	
	9. Los logaritmos comunes son logaritmos de base 2, 5 ó 10.	
	10. Un logaritmo natural es un logaritmo de base e.	
	11. La desintegración exponencial es cuando una cantidad disminuye en una cantidad fija durante cierto período de tiempo.	
	12. El porcentaje de aumento en un problema de crecimiento exponencial se llama *tasa de crecimiento*.	

PASO 2   *Después de completar el Capítulo 8*

- Vuelve a leer cada enunciado y completa la última columna con una A o una D.

- ¿Cambió cualquiera de tus opiniones sobre los enunciados de la primera columna?

- En una hoja de papel aparte, escribe un ejemplo de por qué estás en desacuerdo con los enunciados que marcaste con una D.

8-1 Study Guide and Intervention

Graphing Exponential Functions

Lesson 8-1

Exponential Growth An **exponential growth function** has the form $y = b^x$, where $b > 1$. The graphs of exponential equations can be transformed by changing the value of the constants a, h, and k in the exponential equation: $f(x) = ab^{x-h} + k$.

Parent Function of Exponential Growth Functions, $f(x) = b^x, b > 1$	1. The function is continuous, one-to-one, and increasing. 2. The domain is the set of all real numbers. 3. The x-axis is the asymptote of the graph. 4. The range is the set of all non-zero real numbers. 5. The graph contains the point (0, 1).

Example Graph $y = 4^x + 2$. State the domain and range.

Make a table of values. Connect the points to form a smooth curve.

x	−1	0	1	2	3
y	2.25	3	6	18	66

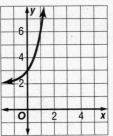

The domain of the function is all real numbers, while the range is the set of all positive real numbers greater than 2.

Exercises

Graph each function. State the domain and range.

1. $y = 3(2)^x$

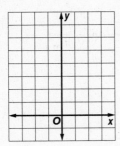

2. $y = \frac{1}{3}(3)^x$

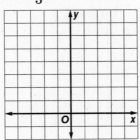

3. $y = 0.25(5)^x$

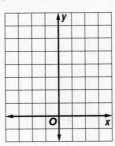

4. $y = 2(3)^x$

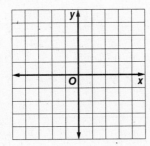

5. $y = 4^x - 2$

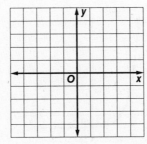

6. $y = 2^{x+5}$

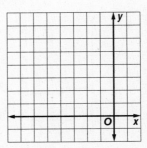

8-1 Study Guide and Intervention *(continued)*

Graphing Exponential Functions

Exponential Decay The following table summarizes the characteristics of **exponential decay** functions.

Parent Function of Exponential Decay Functions, $f(x) = b^x, 0 < b < 1$	1. The function is continuous, one-to-one, and decreasing. 2. The domain is the set of all real numbers. 3. The x-axis is the asymptote of the graph. 4. The range is the set of all positive real numbers. 5. The graph contains the point (0, 1).

Example Graph $y = \left(\frac{1}{2}\right)^x$. **State the domain and range.**

Make a table of values. Connect the points to form a smooth curve. The domain is all real numbers and the range is the set of all positive real numbers.

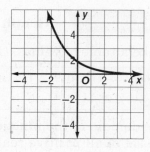

x	–2	–1	0	1	2
y	4	2	1	0.5	0.25

Exercises

Graph each function. State the domain and range.

1. $y = 6\left(\frac{1}{2}\right)^x$

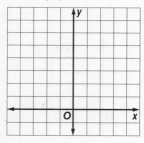

2. $y = -2\left(\frac{1}{4}\right)^x$

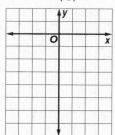

3. $y = -0.4(0.2)^x$

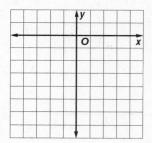

4. $y = \left(\frac{2}{5}\right)\left(\frac{1}{2}\right)^{x-1} + 2$

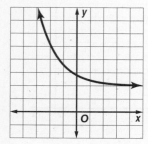

5. $y = 4\left(\frac{1}{5}\right)^{x+3} - 1$

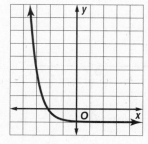

6. $y = \left(-\frac{1}{3}\right)\left(\frac{3}{4}\right)^{x-5} + 6$

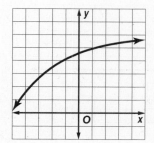

8-1 Skills Practice

Graphing Exponential Functions

Graph each function. State the function's domain and range.

1. $y = 3(2)^x$

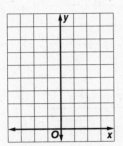

2. $y = 2\left(\frac{1}{2}\right)^x$

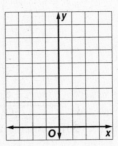

3. $y = -\frac{3}{2}(1.5)^x$

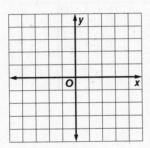

4. $y = 3\left(\frac{1}{3}\right)^x$

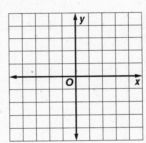

For each graph $f(x)$ is the parent function and $g(x)$ is a transformation of $f(x)$. Use the graph to determine $g(x)$.

5. $f(x) = 4^x$

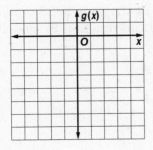

6. $f(x) = \left(\frac{1}{5}\right)^x$

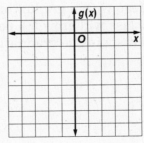

Lesson 8-1

8-1 Practice

Graphing Exponential Functions

Graph each function. State the domain and range.

1. $y = 1.5(2)^x$

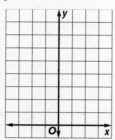

2. $y = 4(3)^x$

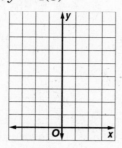

3. $y = 3(0.5)^x$

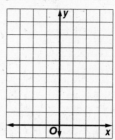

4. $y = 5\left(\dfrac{1}{2}\right)^x - 8$

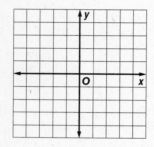

5. $y = -2\left(\dfrac{1}{4}\right)^{x-3}$

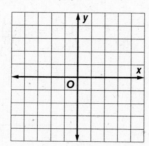

6. $y = \dfrac{1}{2}(3)^{x+4} - 5$

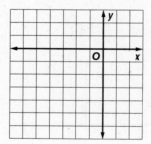

7. BIOLOGY The initial number of bacteria in a culture is 12,000. The culture doubles each day.

  a. Write an exponential function to model the population y of bacteria after x days.

  b. How many bacteria are there after 6 days?

8. EDUCATION A college with a graduating class of 4000 students in the year 2008 predicts that its graduating class will grow 5% per year. Write an exponential function to model the number of students y in the graduating class t years after 2008.

8-1 Word Problem Practice

Graphing Exponential Functions

1. **GOLF BALLS** A golf ball manufacturer packs 3 golf balls into a single package. Three of these packages make a gift box. Three gift boxes make a value pack. The display shelf is high enough to stack 3 value packs one on top of the other. Three such columns of value packs make up a display front. Three display fronts can be packed in a single shipping box and shipped to various retail stores. How many golf balls are in a single shipping box?

2. **FOLDING** Paper thickness ranges from 0.0032 inch to 0.0175 inch. Kay folds a piece of paper 0.01 inch thick in half over and over until it is at least 25 layers thick. How many times does she fold the paper in half and how many layers are there? How thick is the folded paper?

3. **SUBSCRIPTIONS** Subscriptions to an online arts and crafts club have been increasing by 20% every year. The club began with 40 members.

Year	0	1	2	3	4
Subscriptions	40	48			

Make a graph of the number of subscribers over the first 5 years of the club's existence.

4. **TENNIS SHOES** The cost of a pair of tennis shoes increases about 5.1% every year. About how much would a $50 pair of tennis shoes cost 25 years from now?

5. **MONEY** Sam opened a savings account that compounds interest at a rate of 3% annually. Let P be the initial amount Sam deposited and let t be the number of years the account has been open.

a. Write an equation to find A, the amount of money in the account after t years. Assume that Sam made more additional deposits and no withdrawals.

b. If Sam opened the account with $500 and made no deposits or withdrawals, how much is in the account 10 years later?

c. What is the least number of years it would take for such an account to double in value?

Lesson 8-1

8-1 | Enrichment

Families of Curves

Use these graphs for the problems below.

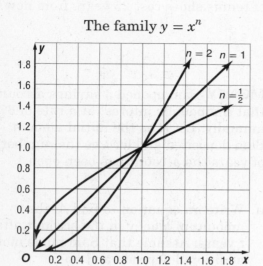

The family $y = x^n$

The family $y = e^{mx}$

1. Use the graph on the left to describe the relationship among the curves $y = x^{\frac{1}{2}}$, $y = x^1$, and $y = x^2$.

2. Graph $y = x^n$ for $n = \frac{1}{10}, \frac{1}{4}, 4$, and 10 on the grid with $y = x^{\frac{1}{2}}$, $y = x^1$, and $y = x^2$.

3. Which two regions in the first quadrant contain no points of the graphs of the family for $y = x^n$?

4. On the right grid, graph the members of the family $y = e^{mx}$ for which $m = 1$ and $m = -1$. The number e is irrational. It is about 2.71828. Use a calculator to evaluate the function and complete the graphs.

5. Describe the relationship among these two curves and the y-axis.

6. Graph $y = e^{mx}$ for $m = 0, \pm\frac{1}{4}, \pm\frac{1}{2}, \pm2$, and ±4.

8-1 Graphing Calculator Activity

Regression Equation Lab

A graphing calculator can be used to determine a regression equation that best fits a set of data. This activity requires tiles labeled on one side, and a container.

Collect the Data

Step 1 Place the tiles on the desktop and count the total number. Record the total number. Then place the tiles in the container and gently shake.

Step 2 Pour the tiles onto the desktop, remove all the tiles with a label showing, and set these aside. Count the remaining tiles without the labels showing and return them to the container.

Step 3 Record the data in a table like this one.

Trials x	Number of tiles without label showing y
1	
2	

Step 4 Repeat step 2 and 3 until the number of tiles without labels is zero or the number remains constant.

Step 5 Take the tiles that were set aside in Step 2 and pour them out of the container onto the desktop. Remove the tiles without the label showing and count the tiles with the label showing. Repeat this process until all the tiles have been removed.

Step 6 Record the data in a table like this one.

Trials x	Number of tiles without label showing y
1	
2	

Analyze the Data

1. Use [STAT] to enter trials in **L1** and number of tiles without label showing in **L2**. Enter trials in **L3** and number of tiles with the label showing in **L4**.

2. Use **[STATPLOT]** to make a scatter plot. Make a graph on paper for each plot. Record the window used. Describe the pattern of the points.

3. From the [STAT] **[CALC]** menu find the regression equation that best fits the data. Record the two closest equations, rounding values to the nearest hundredths. List and discuss the r and/or r^2 values. Also include the graphs in determining the best-fitting regression equation.

4. Sketch your best-fit regression equation choice for each scatter-plot on paper.

5. Describe any problems with the data or the regression equations.

6. Insert (0, total number of tiles) in the tables and the lists. Describe the effect on the graphs. What happens with **[PwrReg]** and **[ExpReg]** when this ordered pair is inserted? Explain why this occurs.

Lesson 8-1

8-2 Study Guide and Intervention

Solving Exponential Equations and Inequalities

Solve Exponential Equations All the properties of rational exponents that you know also apply to real exponents. Remember that $a^m \cdot a^n = a^{m+n}$, $(a^m)^n = a^{mn}$, and $a^m \div a^n = a^{m-n}$.

Property of Equality for Exponential Functions	If b is a positive number other than 1, then $b^x = b^y$ if and only if $x = y$.

Example 1 Solve $4^{x-1} = 2^{x+5}$.

$4^{x-1} = 2^{x+5}$	Original equation
$(2^2)^{x-1} = 2^{x+5}$	Rewrite 4 as 2^2.
$2(x-1) = x+5$	Prop. of Inequality for Exponential Functions
$2x - 2 = x + 5$	Distributive Property
$x = 7$	Subtract x and add 2 to each side.

Example 2 Write an exponential function whose graph passes through the points (0, 3) and (4, 81).

The y-intercept is (0, 3), so $a = 3$. Since the other point is (4, 81), $b = \sqrt[4]{\dfrac{81}{3}}$.

Simplifying $\sqrt[4]{\dfrac{81}{3}} = \sqrt[4]{27} \approx 2.280$, the equation is $y = 3(2.280)^x$.

Exercises

Solve each equation.

1. $3^{2x-1} = 3^{x+2}$

2. $2^{3x} = 4^{x+2}$

3. $3^{2x-1} = \dfrac{1}{9}$

4. $4^{x+1} = 8^{2x+3}$

5. $8^{x-2} = \dfrac{1}{16}$

6. $25^{2x} = 125^{x+2}$

7. $9^{x+1} = 27^{x+4}$

8. $36^{2x+4} = 216^{x+5}$

9. $\left(\dfrac{1}{64}\right)^{x-2} = 16^{3x+1}$

Write an exponential function for the graph that passes through the given points.

10. (0, 4) and (2, 36)

11. (0, 6) and (1, 81)

12. (0, 5) and (6, 320)

13. (0, 2) and (5, 486)

14. (0, 8) and $\left(3, \dfrac{27}{8}\right)$

15. (0, 1) and (4, 625)

16. (0, 3) and (3, 24)

17. (0, 12) and (4, 144)

18. (0, 9) and (2, 49)

8-2 Study Guide and Intervention (continued)

Solve Exponential Equations and Inequalities

Solve Exponential Inequalities An **exponential inequality** is an inequality involving exponential functions.

Property of Inequality for Exponential Functions	If $b > 1$ then $b^x > b^y$ if and only if $x > y$ and $b^x < b^y$ if and only if $x < y$.

Example Solve $5^{2x-1} > \dfrac{1}{125}$.

$5^{2x-1} > \dfrac{1}{125}$ Original inequality

$5^{2x-1} > 5^{-3}$ Rewrite $\dfrac{1}{125}$ as 5^{-3}.

$2x - 1 > -3$ Prop. of Inequality for Exponential Functions

$2x > -2$ Add 1 to each side.

$x > -1$ Divide each sidet by 2.

The solution set is $\{x \mid x > -1\}$.

Exercises

Solve each inequality.

1. $3^{x-4} < \dfrac{1}{27}$

2. $4^{2x-2} > 2^{x+1}$

3. $5^{2x} < 125^{x-5}$

4. $10^{4x+1} > 100^{x-2}$

5. $7^{3x} < 49^{1-x}$

6. $8^{2x-5} < 4^{x+8}$

7. $16 \geq 4^{x+5}$

8. $\left(\dfrac{1}{27}\right)^{2x+1} \leq \left(\dfrac{1}{243}\right)^{3x-2}$

9. $\left(\dfrac{1}{2}\right)^{x-3} > 8^{2x}$

10. $\dfrac{1}{81} < 9^{2x-4}$

11. $32^{3x-4} > 128^{4x+3}$

12. $27^{2x-5} < \left(\dfrac{1}{9}\right)^{5x}$

13. $\left(\dfrac{1}{25}\right)^{2x-1} \leq 125^{3x+1}$

14. $\left(\dfrac{7}{343}\right)^{x-3} \geq \left(\dfrac{1}{49}\right)^{2x+1}$

15. $\left(\dfrac{9}{27}\right)^{6x-1} \geq \left(\dfrac{27}{9}\right)^{-x+6}$

Lesson 8-2

8-2 Skills Practice

Solving Exponential Equations and Inequalities

Solve each equation.

1. $25^{2x+3} = 25^{5x-9}$

2. $9^{8x-4} = 81^{3x+6}$

3. $4^{x-5} = 16^{2x-31}$

4. $4^{3x-3} = 8^{4x-4}$

5. $9^{-x+5} = 27^{6x-10}$

6. $125^{3x-4} = 25^{4x+2}$

Solve each inequality.

7. $\left(\dfrac{1}{36}\right)^{6x-3} > 6^{3x-9}$

8. $64^{4x-8} < 256^{2x+6}$

9. $\left(\dfrac{1}{27}\right)^{3x+13} \le 9^{5x-\frac{1}{2}}$

10. $\left(\dfrac{1}{9}\right)^{2x+7} \le 27^{6x-12}$

11. $\left(\dfrac{1}{8}\right)^{-2x-6} > \left(\dfrac{1}{32}\right)^{-x+11}$

12. $9^{9x+1} < \left(\dfrac{1}{243}\right)^{-3x+5}$

Write an exponential function whose graph passes through the given points.

13. $(0, 3)$ and $(3, 375)$

14. $(0, -1)$ and $(6, -64)$

15. $(0, 7)$ and $(-2, 28)$

16. $\left(0, \dfrac{1}{2}\right)$ and $(2, 40.5)$

17. $(0, 15)$ and $(1, 12)$

18. $(0, -6)$ and $(-4, -1536)$

19. $\left(0, \dfrac{1}{3}\right)$ and $(3, 9)$

20. $(0, 1)$ and $(6, 4096)$

21. $(0, -2)$ and $(-1, -4)$

8-2 Practice

Solving Exponential Equations and Inequalities

Solve each equation.

1. $4^{x+35} = 64^{x-3}$

2. $\left(\frac{1}{64}\right)^{0.5x-3} = 8^{9x-2}$

3. $3^{x-4} = 9^{x+28}$

4. $\left(\frac{1}{4}\right)^{2x+2} = 64^{x-1}$

5. $\left(\frac{1}{2}\right)^{x-3} = 16^{3x+1}$

6. $3^{6x-2} = \left(\frac{1}{9}\right)^{x+1}$

Write an exponential function for the graph that passes through the given points.

7. $(0, 5)$ and $(4, 3125)$

8. $(0, 8)$ and $(4, 2048)$

9. $\left(0, \frac{3}{4}\right)$ and $(2, 36.75)$

10. $(0, -0.2)$ and $(-3, -3.125)$

11. $(0, 15)$ and $\left(2, \frac{15}{16}\right)$

12. $(0, 0.7)$ and $\left(\frac{1}{2}, 3.5\right)$

Solve each inequality.

13. $400 > \left(\frac{1}{20}\right)^{7x+8}$

14. $10^{2x+7} \geq 1000^{x}$

15. $\left(\frac{1}{16}\right)^{3x-4} \leq 64^{x-1}$

16. $\left(\frac{1}{8}\right)^{x-6} < 4^{4x+5}$

17. $\left(\frac{1}{36}\right)^{x+8} \leq 216^{x-3}$

18. $128^{x+3} < \left(\frac{1}{1024}\right)^{2x}$

19. At time t, there are 216^{t+18} bacteria of type A and 36^{2t+8} bacteria of type B organisms in a sample. When will the number of each type of bacteria be equal?

Lesson 8-2

8-2 Word Problem Practice

Solving Exponential Equations and Inequalities

1. BANKING The certificate of deposit that Siobhan bought on her birthday pays interest according to the formula $A = 1200 \left(1 + \frac{0.052}{12}\right)^{48}$. What is the annual interest rate?

2. INTEREST Marty invested $2000 in an account that pays at least 4% annual interest. He wants to see how much money he will have over the next few years. Graph the inequality $y \geq 2000(1 + 0.04)^x$ to show his potential earnings.

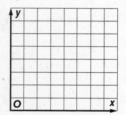

3. BUSINESS Ahmed's consulting firm began with 23 clients. After 7 years, he now has 393 clients. Write an exponential equation describing the firm's growth.

4. POPULATION In 2000, the world population was calculated to be 6,071,675,206. In 2008, it was 6,679,493,893. Write an exponential equation to model the growth of the world population over these 8 years. Round the base to the nearest thousandth.
Source: U.S. Census Bureau

5. BUSINESS Ingrid and Alberto each opened a business in 2000. Ingrid started with 2 employees and in 2003 she had 50 employees. Alberto began with 32 employees and in 2007 he had 310 employees. Since 2000, each company has experienced exponential growth.

a. Write an exponential equation representing the growth for each business.

b. Calculate the number of employees each company had in 2005.

c. Is it reasonable to expect that a business can experience exponential growth? Explain your answer.

8-2 Enrichment

Richter Scale

In 1935, Charles Richter and Beno Gutenberg working in California recognized that seismic waves that are radiated by earthquakes could be a way to estimate the magnitude or strength of an earthquake. Using a piece of equipment known as a Wood-Anderson seismograph, they developed the Richter scale. They discovered that the magnitude of an earthquake is equal to the base-10 logarithm of the amplitude of the wave recorded by the seismograph plus a correction factor based on the location of the seismograph or $M = \log_{10} A + CF$. With the magnitude, the amount of seismic energy in erg of the earthquake can be calculated using the formula $E_s = 10^{11.8 \, + \, 1.5M}$.

1. The largest earthquake ever recorded was in Chile in 1960. It released about $1.995 + 10^{25}$ erg.

   a. On the Richter scale what was the magnitude of this earthquake? Round to the nearest tenth.

   b. Assume that the seismograph that records this has a correction factor of 6.2, what would be the amplitude of wave recorded by the seismograph? Round to the nearest hundredth.

2. The amount of seismic energy released divided by 6.4×10^8 would give the number of ounces of TNT (dynamite) needed for a comparable destructive force.

   a. The largest thermonuclear weapon created has a destructive force of 32 million tons of dynamite. How many ergs is this?

   b. What would be the magnitude of this force on the Richter scale?

3. Using dynamite in a lab a rock is broken and the results are recorded with a seismograph. Assuming a correction factor of .3, there was an amplitude of about 0.0158.

   a. What would be the magnitude of this on the Richter scale?

   b. How much seismic energy would be released by this action? Express your answer in scientific notation.

   c. How many ounces of dynamite were used?

Lesson 8-2

8-2 Graphing Calculator Activity

Solving Exponential Equations and Inequalities

Exponential equations and inequalities can be solved on a graphing calculator or on a TI–Nspire.

Example Solve $5^{(2x + 5)} = 125^{(x + 2.5)} - 2$.

Step 1: Enter $5^{(2x + 5)}$ as **Y1** and $125^{(x + 2.5)} - 2$ as **Y2**.

Keystrokes: [Y=] 5 [∧] [(] 2 [X,T,θ,n] [+] 5 [)] [ENTER]
125 [∧] [(] [X,T,θ,n] [+] 2 [.] 5 [)] [−] 2 [ENTER]

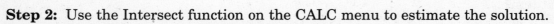

Then graph the two equations.

Keystrokes: [GRAPH]

Step 2: Use the Intersect function on the CALC menu to estimate the solution.

Keystrokes: [2nd] [CALC] 5 [ENTER] [ENTER] [ENTER]

The intersection is at approximately (−2.17, 2.88).

Check your solution: Substituting −2.17 for x, $5^{(0.66)} \approx 125^{(0.33)} - 2$.

Exercises

Solve each exponential equation or inequality with a graphing calculator.

1. $3^{4x + 7} = 27^{4x - 3}$

2. $16^{2x + 5} > 64^{3x - 2}$

3. $343^{2x - 9} = 49^{x + 6}$

4. $128^{x - 5} < 16^{2x - 5}$

5. $625^{3x - 1} = 25^{3x + 4}$

6. $3^{x + 1} = 6^{x - 2}$

7. $16^{2x - 1} - 4 = 8^{-x + 2}$

8. $3^{2x} = 4^{x - 1}$

8-3 Study Guide and Intervention

Logarithms and Logarithmic Functions

Logarithmic Functions and Expressions

Definition of Logarithm with Base b	Let b and x be positive numbers, $b \neq 1$. The logarithm of x with base b is denoted $\log_b x$ and is defined as the exponent y that makes the equation $b^y = x$ true.

The inverse of the exponential function $y = b^x$ is the **logarithmic function** $x = b^y$. This function is usually written as $y = \log_b x$.

Example 1 Write an exponential equation equivalent to $\log_3 243 = 5$.

$3^5 = 243$

Example 2 Write a logarithmic equation equivalent to $6^{-3} = \dfrac{1}{216}$.

$\log_6 \dfrac{1}{216} = -3$

Example 3 Evaluate $\log_8 16$.

$8^{\frac{4}{3}} = 16$, so $\log_8 16 = \dfrac{4}{3}$.

Exercises

Write each equation in exponential form.

1. $\log_{15} 225 = 2$

2. $\log_3 \dfrac{1}{27} = -3$

3. $\log_4 32 = \dfrac{5}{2}$

Write each equation in logarithmic form.

4. $2^7 = 128$

5. $3^{-4} = \dfrac{1}{81}$

6. $\left(\dfrac{1}{7}\right)^3 = \dfrac{1}{343}$

7. $7^{-2} = \dfrac{1}{49}$

8. $2^9 = 512$

9. $64^{\frac{2}{3}} = 16^{\frac{1}{7}}$

Evaluate each expression.

10. $\log_4 64$

11. $\log_2 64$

12. $\log_{100} 100{,}000$

13. $\log_5 625$

14. $\log_{27} 81$

15. $\log_{25} 5$

16. $\log_2 \dfrac{1}{128}$

17. $\log_{10} 0.00001$

18. $\log_4 \dfrac{1}{32}$

Lesson 8-3

8-3 **Study Guide and Intervention** *(continued)*

Logarithms of Logarithmic Functions

Graphing Logarithmic Functions The function $y = \log_b x$, where $b \neq 1$, is called a **logarithmic function.** The graph of $f(x) = \log_b x$ represents a parent graph of the logarithmic functions. Properties of the parent function are described in the following table.

Parent function of Logarithmic Functions, $f(x) = \log_b x$	1. The function is continuous and one-to-one.
	2. The domain is the set of all positive real numbers.
	3. The y-axis is an asymptote of the graph.
	4. The range is the set of all real numbers.
	5. The graph contains the point $(1, 0)$.

The graphs of logarithmic functions can be transformed by changing the value of the constants a, h, and k in the equation $f(x) = a \log_b (x - h) + k$.

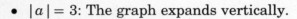

Example **Graph $f(x) = -3 \log_{10} (x - 2) + 1$.**

This is a transformation of the graph of $f(x) = \log_{10} x$.

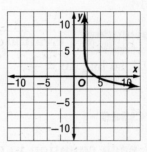

- $|a| = 3$: The graph expands vertically.

- $a < 0$: The graph is reflected across the x-axis.

- $h = 2$: The graph is translated 2 units to the right.

- $k = 1$: The graph is translated 1 unit up.

Exercises

Graph each function.

1. $f(x) = 4 \log_2 x$

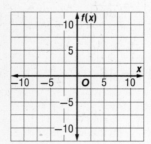

2. $f(x) = 4 \log_3 (x - 1)$

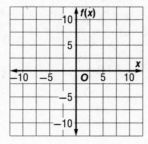

3. $f(x) = 2 \log_4 (x + 3) - 2$

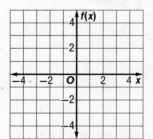

8-3 Skills Practice

Logarithms and Logarithmic Functions

Write each equation in exponential form.

1. $\log_3 243 = 5$

2. $\log_4 64 = 3$

3. $\log_9 3 = \dfrac{1}{2}$

4. $\log_5 \dfrac{1}{25} = -2$

Write each equation in logarithmic form.

5. $2^3 = 8$

6. $3^2 = 9$

7. $8^{-2} = \dfrac{1}{64}$

8. $\left(\dfrac{1}{3}\right)^2 = \dfrac{1}{9}$

Evaluate each expression.

9. $\log_5 25$

10. $\log_9 3$

11. $\log_{10} 1000$

12. $\log_{125} 5$

13. $\log_4 \dfrac{1}{64}$

14. $\log_5 \dfrac{1}{625}$

15. $\log_8 512$

16. $\log_{27} \dfrac{1}{3}$

Graph each function.

17. $f(x) = \log_3(x + 1) - 4$

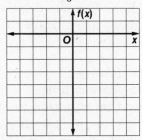

18. $f(x) = -\log_5 x + 2.5$

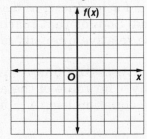

Lesson 8-3

8-3 Practice

Logarithms and Logarithmic Functions

Write each equation in exponential form.

1. $\log_6 216 = 3$ **2.** $\log_2 64 = 6$ **3.** $\log_3 \dfrac{1}{81} = -4$

4. $\log_{10} 0.00001 = -5$ **5.** $\log_{25} 5 = \dfrac{1}{2}$ **6.** $\log_{32} 8 = \dfrac{3}{5}$

Write each equation in logarithmic form.

7. $5^3 = 125$ **8.** $7^0 = 1$ **9.** $3^4 = 81$

10. $3^{-4} = \dfrac{1}{81}$ **11.** $\left(\dfrac{1}{4}\right)^3 = \dfrac{1}{64}$ **12.** $7776^{\frac{1}{5}} = 6$

Evaluate each expression.

13. $\log_3 81$ **14.** $\log_{10} 0.0001$ **15.** $\log_2 \dfrac{1}{16}$ **16.** $\log_{\frac{1}{3}} 27$

17. $\log_9 1$ **18.** $\log_8 4$ **19.** $\log_7 \dfrac{1}{49}$ **20.** $\log_6 6^4$

Graph each function.

21. $f(x) = \log_2 (x - 2)$ **22.** $f(x) = -2 \log_4 x$

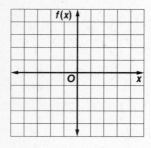   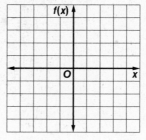

23. SOUND An equation for loudness, in decibels, is $L = 10 \log_{10} R$, where R is the relative intensity of the sound. Sounds that reach levels of 120 decibels or more are painful to humans. What is the relative intensity of 120 decibels?

24. INVESTING Maria invests $1000 in a savings account that pays 4% interest compounded annually. The value of the account A at the end of five years can be determined from the equation $\log_{10} A = \log_{10}[1000(1 + 0.04)^5]$. Write this equation in exponential form.

8-3 Word Problem Practice

Logarithms and Logarithmic Functions

1. **CHEMISTRY** The pH of a solution is found by the formula $pH = -\log H$, where H stands for the hydrogen ion concentration in the formula. What is the pH of a solution to the nearest hundredth when H is 1356?

2. **FIND THE ERROR** Michio wanted to find the value of x in the equation $2(3)^x = 34$. He first converted the equation to $\log_3 2x = 17$. Next he wrote $2x = 3^{17}$ and used a calculator to find $x = 64,570,081$. Was his answer correct? If not, what was his mistake and what is the right answer?

3. **SOUND** The decibel level L of a sound is determined by the formula $L = 10 \log_{10} \dfrac{I}{M}$. Find I in terms of M for a noise with a decibel level of 120.

4. **EARTHQUAKES** The intensity of an earthquake can be measured on the Richter scale using the formula $y = 10^{R-1}$, where y is the absolute intensity of the earthquake and R is its Richter scale measurement.

Richter Scale Number	Absolute Intensity
1	1
2	10
3	100
4	1000
5	10,000

An earthquake in San Francisco in 1906 had an absolute intensity of 6,000,000. What was that earthquake's measurement on the Richter scale?

5. **GAMES** Julio and Natalia decided to play a game in which they each selected a logarithmic function and compare their functions to see which gave larger values. Julio selected the function $f(x) = 10 \log_2 x$ and Natalia selected the function $2 \log_{10} x$.

   a. Which of the functions has a larger value when $x = 7$?

   b. Which of their functions has a larger value when $x = 1$?

   c. Do you think the base or the multiplier is more important in determining the value of a logarithmic function?

Lesson 8-3

8-3 Enrichment

Comparing Logarithmic Graphs

Solve the problems below to relate the graphs of $y = \log_n ax$.

1. Graph the functions $y = \log_2 x$, $y = \log_3 x$, $y = \log_4 x$.

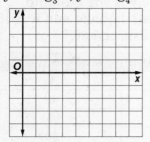

What can you conclude about the graph of $y = \log_n ax$ as the value of n increases and a is constant?

2. Graph the functions $y = \log_2 x$, $y = \log_2 2x$, $y = \log_2 4x$.

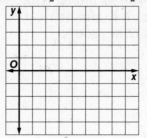

What can you conclude about the graph of $y = \log_n ax$ as the value of a increases and n is constant?

3. Graph the functions $y = \log_2 (-2x)$, $y = \log_2 (-x)$, $y = \log_2 x$, $y = \log_2 2x$.

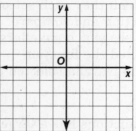

What can you conclude about the graph of $y = \log_n ax$ for a and $-a$ as n stays constant?

4. Graph the functions $y = \log_{\frac{1}{4}} x$, $y = \log_{\frac{1}{2}} x$, $y = \log_2 x$, $y = \log_4 x$.

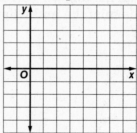

What can you conclude about the graph of $y = \log_n ax$ for n and $\frac{1}{n}$ as s stays constant?

5. Without graphing, describe the graph of $y = \log_{\frac{1}{4}} (-4x)$ using the conclusions you found in Exercises 1–4.

8-3   TI–Nspire Calculator Activity

Logarithms and Logarithmic Functions

Logarithmic functions can be graphed on a graphing calculator or on a TI–Nspire.

Example 1   Graph $y = \log_5 (2x - 3)$.

Use the Graphs and Geometry function from the home menu to enter the equation.

Keystrokes: ⌂ 2 ctrl log₁₀ˣ 5 ▸ 2 ⓧ ÷ 3 enter

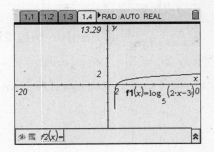

Example 2   Find the intersection of $\log_5(2x - 3)$ and $\log_8(4x + 6)$ by graphing.

On the screen of $\log_5 (2x - 3)$, enter $\log_8 (4x + 6)$ on the $f2(x)$ line.

Keystrokes: ctrl log₁₀ˣ 8 ▸ 4 ⓧ ÷ 6 enter

Now, use the intersection function to find the coordinates of the intersection.

Keystrokes: menu 63

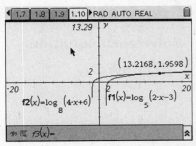

Use the arrow keys to move the pointer ↖ to the graph of $f1(x)$ and click, then move the pointer to the graph of $f2(x)$ and click. Use the arrow keys to move the pointer to the label of the intersection, and hold down the ⓢ button until the open hand on the screen closes (🖐). You can then use the arrow keys to move the label of the intersection until the full coordinates are visible on the TI-Nspire screen.

The intersection point for $\log_5 (2x - 3)$ and $\log_8 (4x + 6)$ is approximately (13.22, 1.96).

Exercises

Graph these logarithmic equations on a TI–Nspire.

1. $y = -3 \log_{18} (x - 9) + 2$ **2.** $y = 4 \log_{11} (2 - x) + 3$ **3.** $y = 4 \log_2 (x - 2) + 2$

4. Find the intersection of $2 \log_7 (x - 3)$ and $\log_4 (2x - 1) - 1$.

Lesson 8-3

8-4 Study Guide and Intervention

Solving Logarithmic Equations and Inequalities

Solving Logarithmic Equations

Property of Equality for Logarithmic Functions	If b is a positive number other than 1, then $\log_b x = \log_b y$ if and only if $x = y$.

Example 1 Solve $\log_2 2x = 3$.

$\log_2 2x = 3$ Original equation

$2x = 2^3$ Definition of logarithm

$2x = 8$ Simplify.

$x = 4$ Simplify.

The solution is $x = 4$.

Example 2 Solve the equation $\log_2 (x + 17) = \log_2 (3 + 23)$.

Since the bases of the logarithms are equal, $(x + 17)$ must equal $(3x + 23)$.

$(x + 17) = (3x + 23)$

$-6 = 2x$

$x = -3$.

Exercises

Solve each equation.

1. $\log_2 32 = 3x$

2. $\log_3 2c = -2$

3. $\log_{2x} 16 = -2$

4. $\log_{25} \left(\frac{x}{2}\right) = \frac{1}{2}$

5. $\log_4 (5x + 1) = 2$

6. $\log_8 (x - 5) = \frac{2}{3}$

7. $\log_4 (3x - 1) = \log_4 (2x + 3)$

8. $\log_2 (x^2 - 6) = \log_2 (2x + 2)$

9. $\log_{x + 4} 27 = 3$

10. $\log_2 (x + 3) = 4$

11. $\log_x 1000 = 3$

12. $\log_8 (4x + 4) = 2$

13. $\log_2 x = \log_2 12$

14. $\log_3 (x - 5) = \log_3 13$

15. $\log_{10} x = \log_{10} (5x - 20)$

16. $\log_5 x = \log_5 (2x - 1)$

17. $\log_4 (x + 12) = \log_4 4x$

18. $\log_6 (x - 3) = \log_6 2x$

8-4 **Study Guide and Intervention** (continued)

Solving Logarithmic Equations and Inequalities

Solving Logarithmic Inequalities

Property of Inequality for Logarithmic Functions	If $b > 1$, $x > 0$, and $\log_b x > y$, then $x > b^y$. If $b > 1$, $x > 0$, and $\log_b x < y$, then $0 < x < b^y$. If $b > 1$, then $\log_b x > \log_b y$ if and only if $x > y$, and $\log_b x < \log_b y$ if and only if $x < y$.

Example 1 Solve $\log_5 (4x - 3) < 3$.

$\log_5 (4x - 3) < 3$ \qquad Original equation

$0 < 4x - 3 < 5^3$ \qquad Property of Inequality

$3 < 4x < 125 + 3$ \qquad Simplify.

$\dfrac{3}{4} < x < 32$ \qquad Simplify.

The solution set is $\left\{ x \mid \dfrac{3}{4} < x < 32 \right\}$.

Example 2 Solve the inequality $\log_3(3x - 4) < \log_3 (x + 1)$.

Since the base of the logarithms are equal to or greater than 1, $3x - 4 < x + 1$.

$2x < 5$

$x < \dfrac{5}{2}$

Since $3x - 4$ and $x + 1$ must both be positive numbers, solve $3x - 4 = 0$ for the lower bound of the inequality.

The solution is $\left\{ x \mid \dfrac{4}{3} < x < \dfrac{5}{2} \right\}$.

Exercises

Solve each inequality.

1. $\log_2 2x > 2$

2. $\log_5 x > 2$

3. $\log_2 (3x + 1) < 4$

4. $\log_4 2x > -\dfrac{1}{2}$

5. $\log_3 (x + 3) < 3$

6. $\log_{27} 6x > \dfrac{2}{3}$

7. $\log_{10} 5x < \log_{10} 30$

8. $\log_{10} x < \log_{10} (2x - 4)$

9. $\log_{10} 3x < \log_{10} (7x - 8)$

10. $\log_2 (8x + 5) > \log_2 (9x - 18)$

11. $\log_{10} (3x + 7) < \log_{10} (7x - 3)$

12. $\log_2 (3x - 4) < \log_2 2x + 7$

Lesson 8-4

8-4 Skills Practice

Solving Logarithmic Equations and Inequalities

Solve each equation.

1. $3x = \log_6 216$

2. $x - 4 = \log_3 243$

3. $\log_4 (4x - 20) = 5$

4. $\log_9 (3 - x) = \log_9 (5x - 15)$

5. $\log_{81} (x + 20) = \log_{81} (6x)$

6. $\log_9 (3x^2) = \log_9 (2x + 1)$

7. $\log_4 (x - 1) = \log_4 (12)$

8. $\log_7 (5 - x) = \log_7 (5)$

9. $\log_x (5x) = 2$

Solve each inequality.

10. $\log_5 (-3x) < 1$

11. $\log_6 x > \log_6 (4 - x)$

12. $\log_{10} (x - 3) < 2$

13. $\log_2 (x - 5) > \log_2 (3)$

14. $\log_7 (8x + 5) > \log_7 (6x - 18)$

15. $\log_9 (3x - 3) < 1.5$

16. $\log_{10} (2x - 2) < \log_{10} (7 - x)$

17. $\log_9 (x - 1) > \log_9 (2x)$

18. $\log_{16} x \geq 0.5$

19. $\log_3\left(\frac{x - 3}{4} + 5\right) > \log_3 (x + 2)$

20. $\log_5 (3x) < \log_5 (2x - 1)$

21. $\log_3 (7 - x) \leq \log_3 (x + 19)$

8-4 Practice

Solving Logarithmic Equations and Inequalities

Solve each equation.

1. $x + 5 = \log_4 256$

2. $3x - 5 = \log_2 1024$

3. $\log_3 (4x - 17) = 5$

4. $\log_5 (3 - x) = 5$

5. $\log_{13} (x^2 - 4) = \log_{13} 3x$

6. $\log_3 (x - 5) = \log_3 (3x - 25)$

Solve each inequality

7. $\log_8 (-6x) < 1$

8. $\log_9 (x + 2) > \log_9 (6 - 3x)$

9. $\log_{11} (x + 7) < 1$

10. $\log_{81} x \le 0.75$

11. $\log_2 (x + 6) < \log_2 17$

12. $\log_{12} (2x - 1) > \log_{12} (5x - 16)$

13. $\log_9 (2x - 1) < 0.5$

14. $\log_{10} (x - 5) > \log_{10} 2x$

15. $\log_3 (x + 12) > \log_3 2x$

16. $\log_3 (0.3x + 5) > \log_3 (x - 2)$

17. $\log_2 (x + 3) < \log_2 (1 - 3x)$

18. $\log_6 (3 - x) \le \log_6 (x - 1)$

19. WILDLIFE An ecologist discovered that the population of a certain endangered species has been doubling every 12 years. When the population reaches 20 times the current level, it may no longer be endangered. Write the logarithmic expression that gives the number of years it will take for the population to reach that level.

Lesson 8-4

8-4   Word Problem Practice
Solving Logarithmic Equations and Inequalities

1. **FISH** The population of silver carp has been growing in the Mississippi River. About every 3 years, the population doubles. Write logarithmic expression that gives the number of years it will take for the population to increase by a factor of ten.

2. **POWERS** Haley tries to solve the equation $\log_4 2x = 5$. She got the wrong answer. What was her mistake? What should the correct answer be?

1.	$\log_4 2x = 5$
2.	$2x = 4^5$
3.	$x = 2^5$
4.	$x = 32$

3. **DIGITS** A computer programmer wants to write a formula that tells how many digits there are in a number n, where n is a positive integer. For example, if $n = 343$, the formula should evaluate to 3 and if $n = 10,000$, the formula should evaluate to 5. Suppose $8 \leq \log_{10} n < 9$. How many digits does n have?

4. **LOGARITHMS** Pauline knows that $\log_b x = 3$ and $\log_b y = 5$. She knows that this is the same as knowing that $b^3 = x$ and $b^5 = y$. Multiply these two equations together and rewrite it as an equation involving logarithms. What is $\log_b xy$?

5. **MUSIC** The first note on a piano keyboard corresponds to a pitch with a frequency of 27.5 cycles per second.

With every successive note you go up the white and black keys of a piano, the pitch multiplies by a factor of $\sqrt[12]{2}$. The formula for the frequency of the pitch sounded when the nth note up the keyboard is played is given by

$$n = 1 + 12 \log_2 \frac{f}{27.5}.$$

a. The pitch that orchestras tune to is the A above middle C. It has a frequency of 440 cycles per second. How many notes up the piano keyboard is this A?

b. Another pitch on the keyboard has a frequency of 1760 cycles per second. How many notes up the keyboard will this be found?

8-4 Enrichment

Musical Relationships

The frequencies of notes that are one octave apart in a musical scale are related by an exponential equation. For the eight C notes on a piano, the equation is $C_n = C_1 2^{n-1}$, where C_n represents the frequency of note C_n.

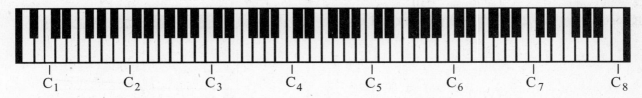

C_1 C_2 C_3 C_4 C_5 C_6 C_7 C_8

1. Find the relationship between C_1 and C_2.

2. Find the relationship between C_1 and C_4.

The frequencies of consecutive notes are related by a common ratio r. The general equation is $f_n = f_1 r^{n-1}$.

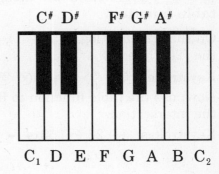

3. If the frequency of middle C is 261.6 cycles per second and the frequency of the next higher C is 523.2 cycles per second, find the common ratio r. (*Hint:* The two C's are 12 notes apart.) Write the answer as a radical expression.

4. Substitute decimal values for r and f_1 to find a specific equation for f_n.

5. Find the frequency of F# above middle C.

6. Frets are a series of ridges placed across the fingerboard of a guitar. They are spaced so that the sound made by pressing a string against one fret has about 1.0595 times the wavelength of the sound made by using the next fret. The general equation is $w_n = w_0(1.0595)^n$. Describe the arrangement of the frets on a guitar.

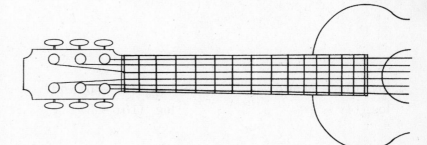

Lesson 8-4

8-4 TI–Nspire Calculator Activity

Evaluating Logarithmic Equations and Inequalities

Logarithmic equations and inequalities can be evaluated on a graphing calculator or on a TI–Nspire.

Example 1 Graph $y = \log_{10}(5x - 1)$ on a graphing calculator.

Keystrokes: ⌂ 2 ctrl log₁₀ˣ 10 ▸ 5 ⊗ ⊙ 1 enter

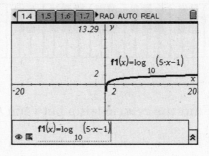

Example 2 Find the intersection of $\log_{10}(5x - 1)$ and $\log_{10}(3x + 2)$ using the table function.

On the screen of $\log_{10}(5x - 1)$, enter $\log_{10}(3x + 2)$ on the $f2(x)$ line.

Keystrokes: ctrl log₁₀ˣ 10 ▸ 3 ⊗ ⊙ 2 enter·

Now, use the table function to find the coordinates of the intersection.

Keystrokes: menu 28 menu 53 ▾ ▾ 0 ⊙ 1 enter

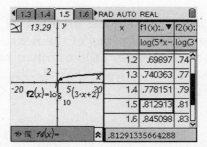

Click the ⊛ button to move past the error message alerting you that there are values for which the logarithmic functions are undefined. Then use the arrow keys to move down the table to find the value where $f1(x)$ equals $f2(x)$. The functions intersect at approximately the point (1.5, 0.81).

Exercises

Estimate the solutions for these logarithmic equations by finding the intersections of the graphs on a TI–Nspire.

1. $\log_{10}(8x + 7)$ and $\log_{10}(15x - 21)$

2. $\log_{10}(x + 1)$ and $\log_{10}(2x - 8)$

3. $\log_{10}(5x + 2)$ and $\log_{10}(10x - 3)$

4. $\log_{10}(3x + 2)$ and $\log_{10}(4x - 3)$

5. $\log_{10}(14x - 5)$ and $\log_{10}(10x - 3)$

6. $\log_{10}(7x - 6)$ and $\log_{10}(3x + 1)$

8-5 Study Guide and Intervention

Properties of Logarithms

Properties of Logarithms Properties of exponents can be used to develop the following properties of logarithms.

Product Property of Logarithms	For all positive numbers a, b, and x, where $x \neq 1$, $\log_x ab = \log_x a + \log_x b$.
Quotient Property of Logarithms	For all positive numbers a, b, and x, where $x \neq 1$, $\log_x \frac{a}{b} = \log_x a - \log_x b$.
Power Property of Logarithms	For any real number p and positive numbers m and b, where $b \neq 1$, $\log_b m^p = p \log_b m$.

Example Use $\log_3 28 \approx 3.0331$ and $\log_3 4 \approx 1.2619$ to approximate the value of each expression.

a. $\log_3 36$

$$\log_3 36 = \log_3 (3^2 \cdot 4)$$
$$= \log_3 3^2 + \log_3 4$$
$$= 2 + \log_3 4$$
$$\approx 2 + 1.2619$$
$$\approx 3.2619$$

b. $\log_3 7$

$$\log_3 7 = \log_3 \left(\frac{28}{4}\right)$$
$$= \log_3 28 - \log_3 4$$
$$\approx 3.0331 - 1.2619$$
$$\approx 1.7712$$

c. $\log_3 256$

$$\log_3 256 = \log_3 (4^4)$$
$$= 4 \cdot \log_3 4$$
$$\approx 4(1.2619)$$
$$\approx 5.0476$$

Exercises

Use $\log_{12} 3 \approx 0.4421$ and $\log_{12} 7 \approx 0.7831$ to approximate the value of each expression.

1. $\log_{12} 21$

2. $\log_{12} \frac{7}{3}$

3. $\log_{12} 49$

4. $\log_{12} 36$

5. $\log_{12} 63$

6. $\log_{12} \frac{27}{49}$

7. $\log_{12} \frac{81}{49}$

8. $\log_{12} 16{,}807$

9. $\log_{12} 441$

Use $\log_5 3 \approx 0.6826$ and $\log_5 4 \approx 0.8614$ to approximate the value of each expression.

10. $\log_5 12$

11. $\log_5 100$

12. $\log_5 0.75$

13. $\log_5 144$

14. $\log_5 \frac{27}{16}$

15. $\log_5 375$

16. $\log_5 1.\overline{3}$

17. $\log_5 \frac{9}{16}$

18. $\log_5 \frac{81}{5}$

Lesson 8-5

8-5 Study Guide and Intervention *(continued)*

Properties of Logarithms

Solve Logarithmic Equations You can use the properties of logarithms to solve equations involving logarithms.

Example Solve each equation.

a. $2 \log_3 x - \log_3 4 = \log_3 25$

$2 \log_3 x - \log_3 4 = \log_3 25$	Original equation
$\log_3 x^2 - \log_3 4 = \log_3 25$	Power Property
$\log_3 \dfrac{x^2}{4} = \log_3 25$	Quotient Property
$\dfrac{x^2}{4} = 25$	Property of Equality for Logarithmic Functions
$x^2 = 100$	Multiply each side by 4.
$x = \pm 10$	Take the square root of each side.

Since logarithms are undefined for $x < 0$, -10 is an extraneous solution. The only solution is 10.

b. $\log_2 x + \log_2 (x + 2) = 3$

$\log_2 x + \log_2 (x + 2) = 3$	Original equation
$\log_2 x(x + 2) = 3$	Product Property
$x(x + 2) = 2^3$	Definition of logarithm
$x^2 + 2x = 8$	Distributive Property
$x^2 + 2x - 8 = 0$	Subtract 8 from each side.
$(x + 4)(x - 2) = 0$	Factor.
$x = 2$ or $x = -4$	Zero Product Property

Since logarithms are undefined for $x < 0$, -4 is an extraneous solution. The only solution is 2.

Exercises

Solve each equation. Check your solutions.

1. $\log_5 4 + \log_5 2x = \log_5 24$

2. $3 \log_4 6 - \log_4 8 = \log_4 x$

3. $\dfrac{1}{2} \log_6 25 + \log_6 x = \log_6 20$

4. $\log_2 4 - \log_2 (x + 3) = \log_2 8$

5. $\log_6 2x - \log_6 3 = \log_6 (x - 1)$

6. $2 \log_4 (x + 1) = \log_4 (11 - x)$

7. $\log_2 x - 3 \log_2 5 = 2 \log_2 10$

8. $3 \log_2 x - 2 \log_2 5x = 2$

9. $\log_3 (c + 3) - \log_3 (4c - 1) = \log_3 5$

10. $\log_5 (x + 3) - \log_5 (2x - 1) = 2$

8-5 Skills Practice

Properties of Logarithms

Use $\log_2 3 \approx 1.5850$ and $\log_2 5 \approx 2.3219$ to approximate the value of each expression.

1. $\log_2 25$

2. $\log_2 27$

3. $\log_2 \frac{3}{5}$

4. $\log_2 \frac{5}{3}$

5. $\log_2 15$

6. $\log_2 45$

7. $\log_2 75$

8. $\log_2 0.6$

9. $\log_2 \frac{1}{3}$

10. $\log_2 \frac{9}{5}$

Solve each equation. Check your solutions.

11. $\log_{10} 27 = 3 \log_{10} x$

12. $3 \log_7 4 = 2 \log_7 b$

13. $\log_4 5 + \log_4 x = \log_4 60$

14. $\log_6 2c + \log_6 8 = \log_6 80$

15. $\log_5 y - \log_5 8 = \log_5 1$

16. $\log_2 q - \log_2 3 = \log_2 7$

17. $\log_9 4 + 2 \log_9 5 = \log_9 w$

18. $3 \log_8 2 - \log_8 4 = \log_8 b$

19. $\log_{10} x + \log_{10} (3x - 5) = \log_{10} 2$

20. $\log_4 x + \log_4 (2x - 3) = \log_4 2$

21. $\log_3 d + \log_3 3 = 3$

22. $\log_{10} y - \log_{10} (2 - y) = 0$

23. $\log_2 r + 2 \log_2 5 = 0$

24. $\log_2 (x + 4) - \log_2 (x - 3) = 3$

25. $\log_4 (n + 1) - \log_4 (n - 2) = 1$

26. $\log_5 10 + \log_5 12 = 3 \log_5 2 + \log_5 a$

Lesson 8-5

8-5 Practice

Properties of Logarithms

Use $\log_{10} 5 \approx 0.6990$ and $\log_{10} 7 \approx 0.8451$ to approximate the value of each expression.

1. $\log_{10} 35$ **2.** $\log_{10} 25$ **3.** $\log_{10} \dfrac{7}{5}$ **4.** $\log_{10} \dfrac{5}{7}$

5. $\log_{10} 245$ **6.** $\log_{10} 175$ **7.** $\log_{10} 0.2$ **8.** $\log_{10} \dfrac{25}{7}$

Solve each equation. Check your solutions.

9. $\log_7 n = \dfrac{2}{3} \log_7 8$

10. $\log_{10} u = \dfrac{3}{2} \log_{10} 4$

11. $\log_6 x + \log_6 9 = \log_6 54$

12. $\log_8 48 - \log_8 w = \log_8 4$

13. $\log_9 (3u + 14) - \log_9 5 = \log_9 2u$

14. $4 \log_2 x + \log_2 5 = \log_2 405$

15. $\log_3 y = -\log_3 16 + \dfrac{1}{3} \log_3 64$

16. $\log_2 d = 5 \log_2 2 - \log_2 8$

17. $\log_{10} (3m - 5) + \log_{10} m = \log_{10} 2$

18. $\log_{10} (b + 3) + \log_{10} b = \log_{10} 4$

19. $\log_8 (t + 10) - \log_8 (t - 1) = \log_8 12$

20. $\log_3 (a + 3) + \log_3 (a + 2) = \log_3 6$

21. $\log_{10} (r + 4) - \log_{10} r = \log_{10} (r + 1)$

22. $\log_4 (x^2 - 4) - \log_4 (x + 2) = \log_4 1$

23. $\log_{10} 4 + \log_{10} w = 2$

24. $\log_8 (n - 3) + \log_8 (n + 4) = 1$

25. $3 \log_5 (x^2 + 9) - 6 = 0$

26. $\log_{16} (9x + 5) - \log_{16} (x^2 - 1) = \dfrac{1}{2}$

27. $\log_6 (2x - 5) + 1 = \log_6 (7x + 10)$

28. $\log_2 (5y + 2) - 1 = \log_2 (1 - 2y)$

29. $\log_{10} (c^2 - 1) - 2 = \log_{10} (c + 1)$

30. $\log_7 x + 2 \log_7 x - \log_7 3 = \log_7 72$

31. SOUND Recall that the loudness L of a sound in decibels is given by $L = 10 \log_{10} R$, where R is the sound's relative intensity. If the intensity of a certain sound is tripled, by how many decibels does the sound increase?

32. EARTHQUAKES An earthquake rated at 3.5 on the Richter scale is felt by many people, and an earthquake rated at 4.5 may cause local damage. The Richter scale magnitude reading m is given by $m = \log_{10} x$, where x represents the amplitude of the seismic wave causing ground motion. How many times greater is the amplitude of an earthquake that measures 4.5 on the Richter scale than one that measures 3.5?

8-5 Word Problem Practice

Properties of Logarithms

1. MENTAL COMPUTATION Jessica has memorized $\log_5 2 \approx 0.4307$ and $\log_5 3 \approx 0.6826$. Using this information, to the nearest thousandth, what power of 5 is equal to 6?

2. POWERS A chemist is testing a soft drink. The pH of a solution is given by

$$-\log_{10} C,$$

where C is the concentration of hydrogen ions. The pH of a popular soft drink is 2.5. If the concentration of hydrogen ions is increased by a factor of 100, what is the new pH of the solution?

3. LUCKY MATH Frank is solving a problem involving logarithms. He does everything correctly except for one thing. He mistakenly writes

$$\log_2 a + \log_2 b = \log_2 (a + b).$$

However, after substituting the values for a and b in his problem, he amazingly still gets the right answer! The value of a was 11. What must the value of b have been?

4. LENGTHS Charles has two poles. One pole has length equal to $\log_7 21$ and the other has length equal to $\log_7 25$. Express the length of both poles joined end to end as the logarithm of a single number.

5. SIZE Alicia wanted to try to quantify the terms *tiny, small, medium, large, big, huge,* and *humongous*. She picked a number of objects and classified them with these adjectives of size. She noticed that the scale seemed exponential. Therefore, she came up with the following definition. Define S to be $\frac{1}{3}\log_3 V$, where V is volume in cubic feet. Then use the following table to find the appropriate adjective.

S satisfies	Adjective
$-2 \leq S < -1$	tiny
$-1 \leq S < 0$	small
$0 \leq S < 1$	medium
$1 \leq S < 2$	large
$2 \leq S < 3$	big
$3 \leq S < 4$	huge
$4 \leq S < 5$	humongous

a. Derive an expression for S applied to a cube in terms of ℓ where ℓ is the side length of a cube.

b. How many cubes, each one foot on a side, would have to be put together to get an object that Alicia would call "big"?

c. How likely is it that a large object attached to a big object would result in a huge object, according to Alicia's scale?

Lesson 8-5

8-5 Enrichment

Spirals

Consider an angle in standard position with its vertex at a point O called the pole. Its initial side is on a coordinatized axis called the *polar axis*. A point P on the terminal side of the angle is named by the *polar coordinates* (r, θ), where r is the directed distance of the point from O and θ is the measure of the angle. Graphs in this system may be drawn on polar coordinate paper such as the kind shown below.

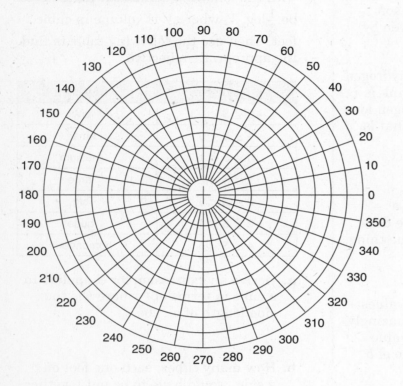

1. Use a calculator to complete the table for $\log_2 r = \dfrac{\theta}{120}$.

   (*Hint:* To find θ on a calculator, press 120 [×] [LOG] r [)] [+] [LOG] 2 [)] .)

r	1	2	3	4	5	6	7	8

2. Plot the points found in Exercise 1 on the grid above and connect to form a smooth curve.

   This type of spiral is called a logarithmic spiral because the angle measures are proportional to the logarithms of the radii.

8-5 TI–Nspire Calculator Activity

Evaluating Logarithms

Logarithms can be evaluated on a TI–Nspire.

Example Solve each equation to the nearest ten-thousandth.

a. $x = 2 \log_3(7) - 3$

Enter the function into the calculator screen on the TI-Nspire.

Keystrokes: 2 (ctrl) (log 10x) 3 ▸ 7 ▸ (c +) 3 (enter)

The solution to $x = 2 \log_3(7) - 3$ is 0.5425.

b. $x = -7 \log_{11}(196) + 3.3 \log_7(247)$

Keystrokes: (ans (-)) 7 (ctrl) (log 10x) 11 ▸ 196 ▸ (c +) 3.3 (enter) (ctrl) (log 10x) 7 ▸ 247 (enter)

The solution of $x = -7 \log_{11}(196) + 3.3 \log_7(247)$ is -6.0648.

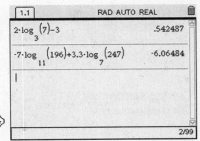

Exercises

Solve each equation to the nearest ten-thousandth.

1. $x = \log_3(87)$

2. $x = \log_2(936)$

3. $x = \log_{11}(19.84)$

4. $\log_9(81)$

5. $x = \log_6(451)$

6. $x = \log_4(76)$

7. $x = \log_7(54) + \log_4(23)$

8. $x = \log_8(22) - \log_{13}(966)$

9. $x = 3\log_{14}(2) - 1.5$

10. $x = \log_4(12) - \log_{12}(4)$

Lesson 8-5

8-6 Study Guide and Intervention

Common Logarithms

Common Logarithms Base 10 logarithms are called **common logarithms**. The expression $\log_{10} x$ is usually written without the subscript as $\log x$. Use the [LOG] key on your calculator to evaluate common logarithms.

The relation between exponents and logarithms gives the following identity.

Inverse Property of Logarithms and Exponents	$10^{\log x} = x$

Example 1 **Evaluate log 50 to the nearest ten-thousandth.**

Use the [LOG] key on your calculator. To four decimal places, $\log 50 = 1.6990$.

Example 2 **Solve $3^{2x+1} = 12$.**

$3^{2x+1} = 12$	Original equation
$\log 3^{2x+1} = \log 12$	Property of Equality for Logarithmic Functions.
$(2x+1)\log 3 = \log 12$	Power Property of Logarithms
$2x + 1 = \dfrac{\log 12}{\log 3}$	Divide each side by log 3.
$2x = \dfrac{\log 12}{\log 3} - 1$	Subtract 1 from each side.
$x = \dfrac{1}{2}\left(\dfrac{\log 12}{\log 3} - 1\right)$	Multiply each side by $\frac{1}{2}$.
$x = \dfrac{1}{2}\left(\dfrac{1.0792}{0.4771} - 1\right)$	Use a calculator.
$x \approx 0.6309$	

Exercises

Use a calculator to evaluate each expression to the nearest ten-thousandth.

1. $\log 18$ **2.** $\log 39$ **3.** $\log 120$

4. $\log 5.8$ **5.** $\log 42.3$ **6.** $\log 0.003$

Solve each equation or inequality. Round to the nearest ten-thousandth.

7. $4^{3x} = 12$ **8.** $6^{x+2} = 18$

9. $5^{4x-2} = 120$ **10.** $7^{3x-1} \geq 21$

11. $2.4^{x+4} = 30$ **12.** $6.5^{2x} \geq 200$

13. $3.6^{4x-1} = 85.4$ **14.** $2^{x+5} = 3^{x-2}$

15. $9^{3x} = 4^{5x+2}$ **16.** $6^{x-5} = 2^{7x+3}$

8-6 Study Guide and Intervention *(continued)*

Common Logarithms

Change of Base Formula The following formula is used to change expressions with different logarithmic bases to common logarithm expressions.

Change of Base Formula	For all positive numbers a, b, and n, where $a \neq 1$ and $b \neq 1$, $\log_a n = \dfrac{\log_b n}{\log_b a}$

Example **Express $\log_8 15$ in terms of common logarithms. Then round to the nearest ten-thousandth.**

$\log_8 15 = \dfrac{\log_{10} 15}{\log_{10} 8}$ Change of Base Formula

$\qquad \approx 1.3023$ Simplify.

The value of $\log_8 15$ is approximately 1.3023.

Exercises

Express each logarithm in terms of common logarithms. Then approximate its value to the nearest ten-thousandth.

1. $\log_3 16$ **2.** $\log_2 40$ **3.** $\log_5 35$

4. $\log_4 22$ **5.** $\log_{12} 200$ **6.** $\log_2 50$

7. $\log_5 0.4$ **8.** $\log_3 2$ **9.** $\log_4 28.5$

10. $\log_3 (20)^2$ **11.** $\log_6 (5)^4$ **12.** $\log_8 (4)^5$

13. $\log_5 (8)^3$ **14.** $\log_2 (3.6)^6$ **15.** $\log_{12} (10.5)^4$

16. $\log_3 \sqrt{150}$ **17.** $\log_4 \sqrt[3]{39}$ **18.** $\log_5 \sqrt[4]{1600}$

8-6 Skills Practice

Common Logarithms

Use a calculator to evaluate each expression to the nearest ten-thousandth.

1. log 6

2. log 15

3. log 1.1

4. log 0.3

Solve each equation or inequality. Round to the nearest ten-thousandth.

5. $3^x > 243$

6. $16^v \leq \frac{1}{4}$

7. $8^p = 50$

8. $7^y = 15$

9. $5^{3b} = 106$

10. $4^{5k} = 37$

11. $12^{7p} = 120$

12. $9^{2m} = 27$

13. $3^{r-5} = 4.1$

14. $8^{y+4} > 15$

15. $7.6^{d+3} = 57.2$

16. $0.5^{t-8} = 16.3$

17. $42^{x^2} = 84$

18. $5^{x^2+1} = 10$

Express each logarithm in terms of common logarithms. Then approximate its value to the nearest ten-thousandth.

19. $\log_3 7$

20. $\log_5 66$

21. $\log_2 35$

22. $\log_6 10$

23. Use the formula pH = −log[$H+$] to find the pH of each substance given its concentration of hydrogen ions.

   a. gastric juices: [$H+$] = 1.0×10^{-1} mole per liter

   b. tomato juice: [$H+$] = 7.94×10^{-5} mole per liter

   c. blood: [$H+$] = 3.98×10^{-8} mole per liter

   d. toothpaste: [$H+$] = 1.26×10^{-10} mole per liter

8-6 Practice

Common Logarithms

Use a calculator to evaluate each expression to the nearest ten-thousandth.

1. $\log 101$

2. $\log 2.2$

3. $\log 0.05$

Use the formula pH $= -\log[H+]$ to find the pH of each substance given its concentration of hydrogen ions.

4. milk: $[H+] = 2.51 \times 10^{-7}$ mole per liter

5. acid rain: $[H+] = 2.51 \times 10^{-6}$ mole per liter

6. black coffee: $[H+] = 1.0 \times 10^{-5}$ mole per liter

7. milk of magnesia: $[H+] = 3.16 \times 10^{-11}$ mole per liter

Solve each equation or inequality. Round to the nearest ten-thousandth.

8. $2^x < 25$

9. $5^a = 120$

10. $6^z = 45.6$

11. $9^m \geq 100$

12. $3.5^x = 47.9$

13. $8.2^y = 64.5$

14. $2^{b+1} \leq 7.31$

15. $4^{2x} = 27$

16. $2^{a-4} = 82.1$

17. $9^{z-2} > 38$

18. $5^{w+3} = 17$

19. $30^{x^2} = 50$

20. $5^{x^2-3} = 72$

21. $4^{2x} = 9^{x+1}$

22. $2^{n+1} = 5^{2n-1}$

Express each logarithm in terms of common logarithms. Then approximate its value to the nearest ten-thousandth.

23. $\log_5 12$

24. $\log_8 32$

25. $\log_{11} 9$

26. $\log_2 18$

27. $\log_9 6$

28. $\log_7 \sqrt{8}$

29. HORTICULTURE Siberian irises flourish when the concentration of hydrogen ions $[H+]$ in the soil is not less than 1.58×10^{-8} mole per liter. What is the pH of the soil in which these irises will flourish?

30. ACIDITY The pH of vinegar is 2.9 and the pH of milk is 6.6. Approximately how many times greater is the hydrogen ion concentration of vinegar than of milk?

31. BIOLOGY There are initially 1000 bacteria in a culture. The number of bacteria doubles each hour. The number of bacteria N present after t hours is $N = 1000(2)^t$. How long will it take the culture to increase to 50,000 bacteria?

32. SOUND An equation for loudness L in decibels is given by $L = 10 \log R$, where R is the sound's relative intensity. An air-raid siren can reach 150 decibels and jet engine noise can reach 120 decibels. How many times greater is the relative intensity of the air-raid siren than that of the jet engine noise?

8-6 Word Problem Practice

Common Logarithms

1. **OTHER BASES** Jamie needs to figure out what $\log_2 3$ is, but she only has a table of common logarithms. In the table, she finds that $\log_{10} 2 \approx 0.3010$ and $\log_{10} 3 \approx 0.4771$. Using this information, to the nearest thousandth, what is $\log_2 3$?

2. **pH** The pH of a solution is given by
$$-\log_{10} C,$$
where C is the concentration of hydrogen ions in moles per liter. A solution of baking soda creates a hydrogen ion concentration 5×10^{-9} of mole per liter. What is the pH of a solution of baking soda? Round your answer to the nearest tenth.

3. **GRAPHING** The graph of $y = \log_{10} x$ is shown below. Use the fact that
$$\frac{1}{\log_{10} 2} \approx 3.32 \text{ to sketch a graph of}$$
$y = \log_2 x$ on the same graph.

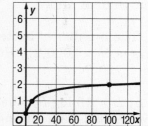

4. **SCIENTIFIC NOTATION** When a number n is written in scientific notation, it has the form $n = s \times 10^p$, where s is a number greater than or equal to 1 and less than 10 and p is an integer. Show that $p \leq \log_{10} n < p + 1$.

5. **LOG TABLE** Marjorie is looking through some old science books owned by her grandfather. At the back of one of them, there is a table of logarithms base 10. However, the book is worn out and some of the entries are unreadable.

Table of Common Logarithms (4 decimal places of accuracy)	
x	$\log_{10} x$
2	0.3010
3	0.4771
4	?
5	0.6989
6	?

a. Approximately what are the missing entries in the table? Round off your answers to the nearest thousandth.

b. How can you use this table to determine $\log_{10} 1.5$?

8-6 Enrichment

The Slide Rule

Before the invention of electronic calculators, computations were often performed on a slide rule. A slide rule is based on the idea of logarithms. It has two movable rods labeled with C and D scales. Each of the scales is logarithmic.

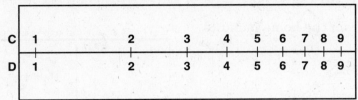

To multiply 2×3 on a slide rule, move the C rod to the right as shown below. You can find 2×3 by adding log 2 to log 3, and the slide rule adds the lengths for you. The distance you get is 0.778, or the logarithm of 6.

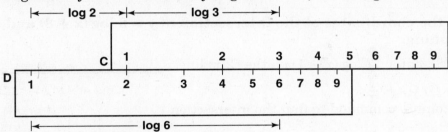

Follow the steps to make a slide rule.

1. Use graph paper that has small squares, such as 10 squares to the inch. Using the scales shown at the right, plot the curve $y = \log x$ for $x = 1, 1.5$, and the whole numbers from 2 through 10. Make an obvious heavy dot for each point plotted.

2. You will need two strips of cardboard. A 5-by-7 index card, cut in half the long way, will work fine. Turn the graph you made in Exercise 1 sideways and use it to mark a logarithmic scale on each of the two strips. The figure shows the mark for 2 being drawn.

3. Explain how to use a slide rule to divide 8 by 2.

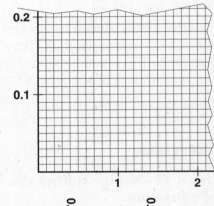

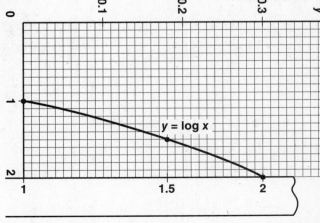

$y = \log x$

8-6 TI–Nspire Calculator Activity

Common Logarithms

Common logarithms are graphed on a TI–Nspire as $\log_{10}$. (On some other graphing calculators, the $\boxed{\text{LOG}}$ key is always defined for common logarithms.)

Example 1   Graph $y = 8 \log (x + 8)$.

Use the Graphs and Geometry function from the home menu to enter the equation.

Keystrokes: 🏠 62 8 (ctrl) (log 10x) 10 ▸ (x) (□ □ +) 8 (enter)

The graph of $y = 8 \log(x + 8)$ is shown at the right.

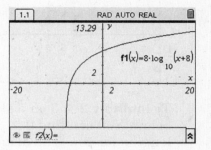

Example 2   Estimate the coordinates of the intersection of $y = 8 \log (x + 8)$ and $y = 17 \log (x - 1)$ by graphing.

On the screen of $8 \log (x + 8)$, enter $17 \log (x - 1)$ on the $f2(x)$ line.

Keystrokes: 17 (ctrl) (log 10x) 10 ▸ (x) (□ □ +) 1 (enter)

Now use the Intersection Point(s) command to find the intersection of the two lines.

Keystrokes: (menu) 63

Use the arrow keys to move the pointer ↖ to the first graph and click the center button ⊙. Then use the arrow keys to move the pointer to the second graph. Click, and the TI–Nspire will display the coordinates of the intersection on screen.

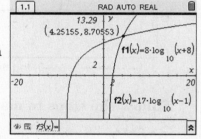

The intersection point of $y = 8 \log(x + 8)$ and $y = 17 \log(x - 1)$ is approximately (4.25, 8.71).

Exercises

Use a TI–Nspire to find the coordinates of the intersection of each pair of equations.

1. $y = 4 \log(3x + 2)$
   $y = -3 \log(x - 4)$

2. $y = 2 \log(2x)$
   $y = 6 \log(x - 7)$

3. $y = -3 \log(2x + 5)$
   $y = -8 \log(x - 9)$

4. $y = \frac{1}{3} \log(4x - 1)$
   $y = -5 \log(3x - 1)$

5. $y = x \log(x)$
   $y = 0.4 \log(-22x + 270)$

6. $y = -3 \log\left(\frac{5}{x}\right)$
   $y = 2 \log(x^3)$

8-7 Study Guide and Intervention

Base e and Natural Logarithms

Base e and Natural Logarithms The irrational number $e \approx 2.71828...$ often occurs as the base for exponential and logarithmic functions that describe real-world phenomena.

Natural Base e	As n increases, $\left(1+\frac{1}{n}\right)^n$ approaches $e \approx 2.71828....$ $\ln x = \log_e x$

The functions $f(x) = e^x$ and $f(x) = \ln x$ are inverse functions.

Inverse Property of Base e and Natural Logarithms	$e^{\ln x} = x$ $\quad$ $\ln e^x = x$

Natural base expressions can be evaluated using the e^x and ln keys on your calculator.

Example 1 Write a logarithmic equation equivalent to $e^{2x} = 7$.

$$e^{2x} = 7 \rightarrow \log_e 7 = 2x$$
$$2x = \ln 7$$

Example 2 Write each logarithmic equation in exponential form.

a. $\ln x \approx 0.3345$

$$\ln x \approx 0.3345 \rightarrow \log_e x \approx 0.3345$$
$$x \approx e^{0.3345}$$

b. $\ln 42 = x$

$$\ln 42 = x \rightarrow \log_e 10 = x$$
$$10 = e^x$$

Exercises

Write an equivalent exponential or logarithmic equation.

1. $e^{15} = x$

2. $e^{3x} = 45$

3. $\ln 20 = x$

4. $\ln x = 8$

5. $e^{-5x} = 0.2$

6. $\ln (4x) = 9.6$

7. $e^{8.2} = 10x$

8. $\ln 0.0002 = x$

Evaluate each logarithm to the nearest ten–thousandth.

9. $\ln 12{,}492$

10. $\ln 50.69$

11. $\ln 9275$

12. $\ln 0.835$

13. $\ln 943 - \ln 181$

14. $\ln 67 + \ln 103$

15. $\ln 931 \cdot \ln 32$

16. $\ln (139 - 45)$

Lesson 8-7

8-7 Study Guide and Intervention (continued)

Base e and Natural Logarithms

Equations and Inequalities with e and ln All properties of logarithms from earlier lessons can be used to solve equations and inequalities with natural logarithms.

Example Solve each equation or inequality.

a. $3e^{2x} + 2 = 10$

$3e^{2x} + 2 = 10$	Original equation
$3e^{2x} = 8$	Subtract 2 from each side.
$e^{2x} = \dfrac{8}{3}$	Divide each side by 3.
$\ln e^{2x} = \ln \dfrac{8}{3}$	Property of Equality for Logarithms
$2x = \ln \dfrac{8}{3}$	Inverse Property of Exponents and Logarithms
$x = \dfrac{1}{2} \ln \dfrac{8}{3}$	Multiply each side by $\frac{1}{2}$.
$x \approx 0.4904$	Use a calculator.

b. $\ln (4x - 1) < 2$

$\ln (4x - 1) < 2$	Original inequality
$e^{\ln (4x - 1)} < e^2$	Write each side using exponents and base e.
$0 < 4x - 1 < e^2$	Inverse Property of Exponents and Logarithms
$1 < 4x < e^2 + 1$	Addition Property of Inequalities
$\dfrac{1}{4} < x < \dfrac{1}{4}(e^2 + 1)$	Multiplication Property of Inequalities
$0.25 < x < 2.0973$	Use a calculator.

Exercises

Solve each equation or inequality. Round to the nearest ten-thousandth.

1. $e^{4x} = 120$

2. $e^x \le 25$

3. $e^{x-2} + 4 = 21$

4. $\ln 6x \ge 4$

5. $\ln (x + 3) - 5 = -2$

6. $e^{-8x} \le 50$

7. $e^{4x-1} - 3 = 12$

8. $\ln (5x + 3) = 3.6$

9. $2e^{3x} + 5 = 2$

10. $6 + 3e^{x+1} = 21$

11. $\ln (2x - 5) = 8$

12. $\ln 5x + \ln 3x > 9$

8-7 Skills Practice

Base e and Natural Logarithms

Write an equivalent exponential or logarithmic equation.

1. $e^x = 3$

2. $e^4 = 8x$

3. $\ln 15 = x$

4. $\ln x \approx 0.6931$

5. $e^4 = x - 3$

6. $\ln 5.34 = 2x$

Write each as a single logarithm.

7. $3 \ln 3 - \ln 9$

8. $4 \ln 16 - \ln 256$

9. $2 \ln x + 2 \ln 4$

10. $3 \ln 4 + 3 \ln 3$

Solve each equation or inequality. Round to the nearest ten-thousandth.

11. $e^x \geq 5$

12. $e^x < 3.2$

13. $2e^x - 1 = 11$

14. $5e^x + 3 = 18$

15. $e^{3x} = 30$

16. $e^{-4x} > 10$

17. $e^{5x} + 4 > 34$

18. $1 - 2e^{2x} = -19$

19. $\ln 3x = 2$

20. $\ln 8x = 3$

21. $\ln (x - 2) = 2$

22. $\ln (x + 3) = 1$

23. $\ln (x + 3) = 4$

24. $\ln x + \ln 2x = 2$

Lesson 8-7

8-7 Practice

Base e and Natural Logarithms

Write an equivalent exponential or logarithmic equation.

1. $\ln 50 = x$

2. $\ln 36 = 2x$

3. $\ln 6 \approx 1.7918$

4. $\ln 9.3 \approx 2.2300$

5. $e^x = 8$

6. $e^5 = 10x$

7. $e^{-x} = 4$

8. $e^2 = x + 1$

Solve each equation or inequality. Round to four decimal places.

9. $e^x < 9$

10. $e^{-x} = 31$

11. $e^x = 1.1$

12. $e^x = 5.8$

13. $2e^x - 3 = 1$

14. $5e^x + 1 \geq 7$

15. $4 + e^x = 19$

16. $-3e^x + 10 < 8$

17. $e^{3x} = 8$

18. $e^{-4x} = 5$

19. $e^{0.5x} = 6$

20. $2e^{5x} = 24$

21. $e^{2x} + 1 = 55$

22. $e^{3x} - 5 = 32$

23. $9 + e^{2x} = 10$

24. $e^{-3x} + 7 \geq 15$

25. $\ln 4x = 3$

26. $\ln(-2x) = 7$

27. $\ln 2.5x = 10$

28. $\ln(x - 6) = 1$

29. $\ln(x + 2) = 3$

30. $\ln(x + 3) = 5$

31. $\ln 3x + \ln 2x = 9$

32. $\ln 5x + \ln x = 7$

33. INVESTING Sarita deposits $1000 in an account paying 3.4% annual interest compounded continuously. Use the formula for continuously compounded interest, $A = Pe^{rt}$, where P is the principal, r is the annual interest rate, and t is the time in years.

a. What is the balance in Sarita's account after 5 years?

b. How long will it take the balance in Sarita's account to reach $2000?

34. RADIOACTIVE DECAY The amount of a radioactive substance y that remains after t years is given by the equation $y = ae^{kt}$, where a is the initial amount present and k is the decay constant for the radioactive substance. If $a = 100$, $y = 50$, and $k = -0.035$, find t.

8-7 Word Problem Practice

Base e and Natural Logarithms

1. **INTEREST** Horatio opens a bank account that pays 2.3% annual interest compounded continuously. He makes an initial deposit of 10,000. What will be the balance of the account in 10 years? Assume that he makes no additional deposits and no withdrawals.

2. **INTEREST** Janie's bank pays 2.8% annual interest compounded continuously on savings accounts. She placed $2000 in the account. How long will it take for her initial deposit to double in value? Assume that she makes no additional deposits and no withdrawals. Round your answer to the nearest quarter year.

3. **BACTERIA** A bacterial population grows exponentially, doubling every 72 hours.

bacteria	x	$2x$	$4x$	$8x$
time	0	72	144	216

Let P be the initial population size and let t be time in hours. Write a formula using the natural base exponential function that gives the size of the population as a function of P and t.

4. **POPULATION** The equation $A = A_0 e^{rt}$ describes the growth of the world's population where A is the population at time t, A_0 is the population at $t = 0$, and r is the annual growth rate. The world's population at the start of 2008 was estimated at 6,641,000,000. If the annual growth rate is 1.2%, when will the world population reach 9 billion?

5. **MONEY MANAGEMENT** Linda wants to invest $20,000. She is looking at two possible accounts. Account A is a standard savings account that pays 3.4% annual interest compounded continuously. Account B would pay her a fixed amount of $200 every quarter.

a. If Linda can invest the money for 5 years only, which account would give her the higher return on her investment? How much more money would she make by choosing the higher paying account?

b. If Linda can invest the money for 10 years only, which account would give her the higher return on her investment? How much more money would she make by choosing the higher paying account?

c. If Linda can invest the money for 20 years only, which account would give her the higher return on her investment? How much more money would she make by choosing the higher paying account?

Lesson 8-7

8-7 Enrichment

Approximations for π and e

The following expression can be used to approximate *e*. If greater and greater values of *n* are used, the value of the expression approximates *e* more and more closely.

$$\left(1 + \frac{1}{n}\right)^n$$

Another way to approximate *e* is to use this infinite sum. The greater the value of *n*, the closer the approximation.

$$e = 1 + 1 + \frac{1}{2} + \frac{1}{2 \cdot 3} + \frac{1}{2 \cdot 3 \cdot 4} + \ldots + \frac{1}{2 \cdot 3 \cdot 4 \cdot \ldots \cdot n} + \ldots$$

In a similar manner, π can be approximated using an infinite product discovered by the English mathematician John Wallis (1616–1703).

$$\frac{\pi}{2} = \frac{2}{1} \cdot \frac{2}{3} \cdot \frac{4}{3} \cdot \frac{4}{5} \cdot \frac{6}{5} \cdot \frac{6}{7} \cdot \ldots \cdot \frac{2n}{2n - 1} \cdot \frac{2n}{2n + 1} \ldots$$

Solve each problem.

1. Use a calculator with an e^x key to find *e* to 7 decimal places.

2. Use the expression $\left(1 + \frac{1}{n}\right)^n$ to approximate *e* to 3 decimal places. Use 5, 100, 500, and 7000 as values of *n*.

3. Use the infinite sum to approximate *e* to 3 decimal places. Use the whole numbers from 3 through 6 as values of *n*.

4. Which approximation method approaches the value of *e* more quickly?

5. Use a calculator with a π key to find π to 7 decimal places.

6. Use the infinite product to approximate π to 3 decimal places. Use the whole numbers from 3 through 6 as values of *n*.

7. Does the infinite product give good approximations for π quickly?

8. Show that $\pi^4 + \pi^5$ is equal to e^6 to 4 decimal places.

9. Which is greater, e^π or π^e?

10. The expression $x^{\frac{1}{x}}$ reaches a maximum value at $x = e$. Use this fact to prove the inequality you found in Exercise 9.

8-8 Study Guide and Intervention

Using Exponential and Logarithmic Functions

Exponential Growth and Decay

Exponential Growth	$f(x) = ae^{kt}$ where a is the initial value of y, t is time in years, and k is a constant representing the **rate of continuous growth**.
Exponential Decay	$f(x) = ae^{-kt}$ where a is the initial value of y, t is time in years, and k is a constant representing **the rate of continuous decay**.

Example POPULATION In 2000, the world population was estimated to be 6.124 billion people. In 2005, it was 6.515 billion.

a. Determine the value of k, the world's relative rate of growth

$y = ae^{kt}$	Formula for continuous growth.
$6.515 = 6.124e^{k(5)}$	$y = 6.515$, $a = 6.124$, and $t = 2005 - 2000$ or 5
$\dfrac{6.515}{6.124} = e^{5k}$	Divide each side by 6.124.
$\ln \dfrac{6.515}{6.124} = \ln e^{5k}$	Property of Equality for Logarithmic Functions.
$\ln \dfrac{6.515}{6.124} = 5k$	$\ln e^x = x$
$0.01238 = k$	Divide each side by 5 and use a calculator.

The world's relative rate of growth is about 0.01238 or 1.2%

b. When will the world's population reach 7.5 billion people?

$7.5 = 6.124e^{0.01238t}$	$y = 7.5$, $a = 6.124$, and $k = 0.01238$
$\dfrac{7.5}{6.124} = e^{0.01238t}$	Divide each side by 6.124.
$\ln \dfrac{7.5}{6.124} = e^{0.01238t}$	Property of Equality for Logarithmic Functions.
$\ln \dfrac{7.5}{6.124} = 0.01238t$	$\ln e^x = x$
$16.3722 = t$	Divide each side by 0.01238 and use a calculator.

The world's population will reach 7.5 billion in 2016

Exercises

1. **CARBON DATING** Use the formula $y = ae^{-0.00012t}$, where a is the initial amount of carbon 14, t is the number of years ago the animal lived, and y is the remaining amount after t years.

   a. How old is a fossil remain that has lost 95% of its Carbon-14?

   b. How old is a skeleton that has 95% of its Carbon-14 remaining?

Lesson 8-8

8-8   Study Guide and Intervention   (continued)

Using Exponential and Logarithmic Functions

Logistic Growth A logistic function models the S-curve of growth of some set λ. The initial stage of growth is approximately exponential; then, as saturation begins, the growth slows, and at some point, growth stops.

Example   **The population of a certain species of fish in a lake after t years is given by $P(t) = \dfrac{1880}{(1 + 1.42e^{-0.037t})}$.**

a. Graph the function.

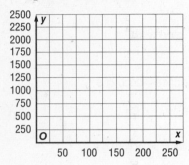

b. Find the horizontal asymptote.

The horizontal asymptote is $P(t) = 1880$.

c. What is the maximum population of the fish in the lake?

By looking at the graph we can tell that the population will reach a ceiling of 1880.

d. When will the population reach 1875?

Replace $P(t)$ by 1875 in the above equation: $1875 = \dfrac{1880}{(1 + 1.42e^{-0.037t})}$

Cross multiply: $1880 = 1875 \cdot (1 + 1.42e^{-0.037t})$

Divide by 1875 on both sides: $1.002667 = (1 + 1.42e^{-0.037t})$

$1.42e^{-0.037t} = -0.002667 \Rightarrow e^{-0.037t} = 0.0018779$

ln both sides: $\ln(e^{-0.037t}) = \ln(0.0018779) \Rightarrow -0.037t = -6.277 \Rightarrow t = 169.66$ yr.

Exercises

1. Assume the population of a specific habitat follows the function: $P(t) = \dfrac{17000}{(1 + 15e^{-0.0082t})}$

     a. Graph the function where $0 \le t \le 500$

     b. What is the horizontal asymptote?

     c. What is the maximum population?

     d. When does the population reach 15,000?

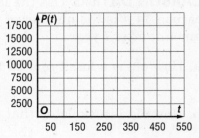

8-8 Skills Practice

Using Exponential and Logarithmic Functions

1. **FISHING** In an over-fished area, the catch of a certain fish is decreasing exponentially. Use $k = 0.084$ to determine how long will it take for the catch to reach half of its current the amount?

2. **POPULATION** A current census shows that the population of a city is 3.5 million. Using the formula $P = ae^{rt}$, find the expected population of the city in 30 years if the growth rate r of the population is 1.5%, a represents the current population in millions, and t represents the time in years.

3. **POPULATION** The population P in thousands of a city can be modeled by the equation $P = 80e^{0.015t}$, where t is the time in years. In how many years will the population of the city be 120,000?

4. **BACTERIA** How many days will it take a culture of bacteria to increase from 2000 to 50,000? Use $k = 0.657$.

5. **NUCLEAR POWER** The element plutonium-239 is highly radioactive. Nuclear reactors can produce and also use this element. The heat that plutonium-239 emits has helped to power equipment on the moon. If the half-life of plutonium-239 is 24,360 years, what is the value of k for this element?

6. **DEPRECIATION** A Global Positioning Satellite (GPS) system uses satellite information to locate ground position. Abu's surveying firm bought a GPS system for $12,500. The GPS is now worth $8600. How long ago did Abu buy the GPS system? Use $k = 0.062$.

7. **LOGISTIC GROWTH** The population of a certain habitat follows the function.

$$p(t) = \frac{105{,}000}{1 + 2.7e^{-0.0981t}}.$$

   a. What is the maximum population of this habitat?

   b. When does the population reach 100,000? Round to the nearest hundredth.

55

Lesson 8-8

8-8 Practice

Using Exponential and Logarithmic Functions

1. **BACTERIA** How many hours will it take a culture of bacteria to increase from 20 to 2000? Use $k = 0.614$.

2. **RADIOACTIVE DECAY** A radioactive substance has a half-life of 32 years. Find the constant k in the decay formula for the substance.

3. **RADIOACTIVE DECAY** Cobalt, an element used to make alloys, has several isotopes. One of these, cobalt 60, is radioactive and has a half-life of 5.7 years. Cobalt 60 is used to trace the path of nonradioactive substances in a system. What is the value of k for cobalt 60?

4. **WHALES** Modern whales appeared 5−10 million years ago. The vertebrae of a whale discovered by paleontologists contain roughly 0.25% as much carbon-14 as they would have contained when the whale was alive. How long ago did the whale die? Use $k = 0.00012$.

5. **POPULATION** The population of rabbits in an area is modeled by the growth equation $P(t) = 8e^{0.26t}$, where P is in thousands and t is in years. How long will it take for the population to reach 25,000?

6. **RADIOACTIVE DECAY** A radioactive element decays exponentially. The decay model is given by the formula $A = A_0e^{-0.04463t}$. A is the amount present after t days and A_0 is the amount present initially. Assume you are starting with 50g. How much of the element remains after 10 days? 30 days?

7. **POPULATION** A population is growing continuously at a rate of 3%. If the population is now 5 million, what will it be in 17 years' time?

8. **BACTERIA** A certain bacteria is growing exponentially according to the model $y = 80e^{kt}$. Using $k = 0.071$, find how many hours it will take for the bacteria reach a population of 10,000 cells?

9. **LOGISTIC GROWTH** The population of a certain habitat follows the function:

$$P(t) = \frac{16,300}{\left(1 + 17.5e^{-0.065t}\right)}$$

   a. What is the maximum population?

   b. When does the population reach 16,200?

8-8 Word Problem Practice

Using Exponential and Logarithmic Functions

1. **PROGRAMMING** For reasons having to do with speed, a computer programmer wishes to model population size using a natural base exponential function. However, the programmer is told that the users of the program will be thinking in terms of the annual percentage increase. Let r be the percentage that the population increases each year. Find the value for k in terms of r so that
$$e^k = 1 + r.$$

2. **CARBON DATING** Archeologists uncover an ancient wooden tool. They analyze the tool and find that it has 22% as much carbon 14 compared to the likely amount that it contained when it was made. Given that the half-life of carbon 14 is about 5730 years, about how old is the artifact? Round your answer to the nearest 100 years.

3. **POPULATION** The doubling time of a population is d years. The population size can be modeled by an exponential equation of the form Pe^{kt}, where P is the initial population size and t is time. What is k in terms of d?

4. **POPULATION** Louisa read that the population of her town has increased steadily at a rate of 2% each year. Today, the population of her town has grown to 68,735.

Population	68,735	67,387	66,066	64,770
Year	Today	−1	−2	−3

Based on this information, what was the population of her town 100 years ago?

5. **CONSUMER AWARENESS** Jason wants to buy a brand new high-definition (HD) television. He could buy one now because he has $7000 to spend, but he thinks that if he waits, the quality of HD televisions will improve. His $7000 earns 2.5% interest annually compounded continuously. The television he wants to buy costs $5000 now, but the cost increases each year by 7%.

a. Write a natural base exponential function that gives the value of Jason's account as a function of time t.

b. Write a natural base exponential function that gives the cost of the television Jason wants as a function of time t.

c. In how many years will the cost of the television exceed the value of the money in Jason's account? In other words, how much time does Jason have to decide whether he wants to buy the television? Round your answer to the nearest tenth of a year.

6. **LOGISTIC GROWTH** The population of a bacteria, in thousands, can be modeled by $P(t) = \dfrac{22{,}000}{(1 + 1.2e^{-k})}$ where t is time in hours and k is a constant.

a. After 1 hour the bacteria population is 10,532, what is the value of k?

b. When does the population reach 21,900?

8-8 Enrichment

Effective Annual Yield

When interest is compounded more than once per year, the effective annual yield is higher than the annual interest rate. The effective annual yield, E, is the interest rate that would give the same amount of interest if the interest were compounded once per year. If P dollars are invested for one year, the value of the investment at the end of the year is $A = P(1 + E)$. If P dollars are invested for one year at a nominal rate r compounded n times per year, the value of the investment at the end of the year is $A = P\left(1 + \frac{r}{n}\right)^n$. Setting the amounts equal and solving for E will produce a formula for the effective annual yield.

$$P(1 + E) = P\left(1 + \frac{r}{n}\right)^n$$

$$1 + E = \left(1 + \frac{r}{n}\right)^n$$

$$E = \left(1 + \frac{r}{n}\right)^n - 1$$

If compounding is continuous, the value of the investment at the end of one year is $A = Pe^r$. Again set the amounts equal and solve for E. A formula for the effective annual yield under continuous compounding is obtained.

$$P(1 + E) = Pe^r$$

$$1 + E = e^r$$

$$E = e^r - 1$$

Example 1   Find the effective annual yield of an investment made at 7.5% compounded monthly.

$r = 0.075$

$n = 12$

$E = \left(1 + \frac{0.075}{12}\right)^{12} - 1 \approx 7.76\%$

Example 2   Find the effective annual yield of an investment made at 6.25% compounded continuously.

$r = 0.0625$

$E = e^{0.0625} - 1 \approx 6.45\%$

Exercises

Find the effective annual yield for each investment.

1. 10% compounded quarterly

2. 8.5% compounded monthly

3. 9.25% compounded continuously

4. 7.75% compounded continuously

5. 6.5% compounded daily (assume a 365-day year)

6. Which investment yields more interest—9% compounded continuously or 9.2% compounded quarterly?

8-8 Spreadsheet Activity

Net Present Value

You have learned how to use exponential and logarithmic functions to perform a number of financial analyses. Spreadsheets can be used to perform many types of analyses, such as calculating the Net Present Value of expenditures or investments. For example, when a business owner is considering a major purchase, it is a good idea to find out whether the investment will be profitable in the future. Consider the example of a local restaurant-delivery service that is debating whether to buy a used van for $8000. The owners of the company estimate that the van will bring in $2500 per year over four years. They can use the following formula to find the present value of the future cash flow to find the Net Present Value (NPV), that is, how much the profits would be worth in today's dollars. $NPV = \dfrac{CF_n}{(1 + r)^n}$, where CF_n = the cash flow in period n and r equals the cost of capital, which is either the interest that will be paid on a loan or the interest that the money would earn if it were invested.

◇	A	B	C	
1	Cost of Asset	$8,000.00		
2	Cost of Capital (r)	0.1		
3				
4	Period (n)	CF	CF/(1+R)^n	
5	1	$2,500.00	$2,272.73	
6	2	$2,500.00	$2,066.12	
7	3	$2,500.00	$1,878.29	
8	4	$2,500.00	$1,707.53	
9			$7,924.66	
10				
11	Total			
12	NPV - Cost	−$75.34		

Sheet 1 / Sheet 2 / Sheet 3 /

Exercises

1. If the NPV is greater than the cost, the investment will pay for itself. Based on the spreadsheet shown above, would it be cost-effective for the company to buy the van? Explain.

2. Four times a year, Josey and Drew publish a magazine. They want to buy a color printer that costs $1750. The cost of capital for this purchase would be 6%. They are planning to raise the price of their magazine from $1 to $2. Create a spreadsheet to determine the NPV for this purchase.

   a. The last issue of the magazine sold 500 copies. If each issue of the magazine printed in color sells 100 copies more than the previous issue, is the printer a good investment after one year? Explain.

   b. If the sales of the magazine continue to rise at the same rate, is the printer a good investment after two years?

3. a. Calculate the NPV for an investment over a period of six years if the cost of capital is 4.5% and the investment will bring a cash flow of $750 every year.

   b. Would this be a good investment of $3000? Explain?

Lesson 8-8

8 Student Recording Sheet

Use this recording sheet with pages 548–549 of the Student Edition.

Multiple Choice

Read each question. Then fill in the correct answer.

1. Ⓐ Ⓑ Ⓒ Ⓓ   5. Ⓐ Ⓑ Ⓒ Ⓓ   9. Ⓐ Ⓑ Ⓒ Ⓓ

2. Ⓕ Ⓖ Ⓗ Ⓙ   6. Ⓕ Ⓖ Ⓗ Ⓙ   10. Ⓐ Ⓑ Ⓒ Ⓓ

3. Ⓐ Ⓑ Ⓒ Ⓓ   7. Ⓐ Ⓑ Ⓒ Ⓓ

4. Ⓕ Ⓖ Ⓗ Ⓙ   8. Ⓕ Ⓖ Ⓗ Ⓙ

Short Response/Gridded Response

Record your answer in the blank.

For gridded response, also enter your answer in the grid by writing each number or symbol in a box. Then fill in the corresponding circle for that number or symbol.

11. _____

12. _____ *(grid in)*

12.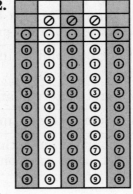

Extended Response

Record your answers for Question 13 on the back of this paper.

Assessment

8 Rubric for Scoring Extended Response

General Scoring Guidelines

- If a student gives only a correct numerical answer to a problem but does not show how he or she arrived at the answer, the student will be awarded only 1 credit. All extended response questions require the student to show work.

- A fully correct answer for a multiple-part question requires correct responses for all parts of the question. For example, if a question has three parts, the correct response to one or two parts of the question that required work to be shown is *not* considered a fully correct response.

- Students who use trial and error to solve a problem must show their method. Merely showing that the answer checks or is correct is not considered a complete response for full credit.

Exercises 14 and 15 Rubric

Score	Specific Criteria
4	For Exercise 14, the correct exponential decay function is set up and explained in part a. For part **b**, the value of t (time) is solved for using the exponential decay formula created in part **a**.
	For Exercise 15, the correct exponential growth function is set up and explained in part a. For part **b**, the value of t (time) is solved for using the exponential growth formula created in part **a**.
3	A generally correct solution, but may contain minor flaws in reasoning or computation.
2	A partially correct interpretation and/or solution to the problem.
1	A correct solution with no supporting evidence or explanation.
0	An incorrect solution indicating no mathematical understanding of the concept or task, or no solution is given.

8   Chapter 8 Quiz 1

(Lessons 8-1 and 8-2)

1. Sketch the graph of $y = 3\left(\frac{1}{2}\right)^x$. Then state the function's domain and range.

1.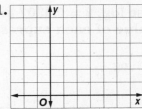

2. Write an exponential function whose graph passes through the points $(0, -5)$ and $(-2, -20)$. Then determine whether the function represents exponential *growth* or *decay*.

3. Solve $\left(\frac{1}{3}\right)^m = 27^{m+2}$.

2. _____

4. Solve $25^{4t+1} \geq 125^{2t}$.

3. _____

5. MULTIPLE CHOICE Solve $6^{2x-1} = 36^{-x}$.

4. _____

    A 0   **B** $\frac{1}{4}$ **C** $\frac{1}{2}$ **D** $\frac{3}{4}$

5. _____

- -

8   Chapter 8 Quiz 2

(Lessons 8-3 and 8-4)

1. Write the equation $81^{\frac{1}{2}} = 9$ in logarithmic form.

1. _____

2. Write the equation $\log_{216} 36 = \frac{2}{3}$ in exponential form.

2. _____

3. Evaluate $\log_{16} 64$.   **4.** Solve $\log_{16} n = -\frac{1}{2}$.

3. _____

5. Solve $\log_5 (4x - 1) \geq \log_5 (x + 2)$.

4. _____

6. Write the equation $3^{-3} = \frac{1}{27}$ in logarithmic form.

5. _____

Solve each equation.

7. $\log_7 36 - \log_7 (2x) = \log_7 4$

6. _____

8. $\log_3 x = \frac{1}{2} \log_3 25 - 5 \log_3 2$

7. _____

9. $\log_5(3x + 4) + \log_5(x - 2) = 3$

8. _____

10. MULTIPLE CHOICE Solve $\log_2 (x + 1) + \log_2 (x - 5) = 4$.

9. _____

    A 5   **B** 6   **C** 7   **D** 8   **10.** _____

8   Chapter 8 Quiz 3

(Lessons 8-5 and 8-6)

SCORE _____

Use $\log_5 2 \approx 0.4307$ and $\log_5 3 \approx 0.6826$ to approximate the value of each expression.

1. _____

1. $\log_5 \dfrac{8}{3}$ 2. $\log_5 24$

2. _____

3. **MULTIPLE CHOICE** Solve $\log_8 x + \log_8 (x + 7) = 1$.

   A -8 **B** -1 **C** 1 **D** 8

3. _____

For Questions 4 and 5, solve each equation or inequality. Round to the nearest ten-thousandth.

4. $4^{2m} = 130$

4. _____

5. $5^{x + 4} = 2^{3x}$

5. _____

---

8   Chapter 8 Quiz 4

(Lessons 8-7 and 8-8)

SCORE _____

1. Write an equivalent logarithmic equation for $e^3 = 2x$.

1. _____

2. Evaluate $e^{\ln 0.3}$.

2. _____

3. A substance decays according to the equation $y = ae^{-0.0025t}$, where t is in minutes. Find the half-life of the substance. Round to the nearest tenth.

3. _____

4. **MULTIPLE CHOICE** In 1925, the population of a city was 90,000. Its population increases by 2.1% per year. What will the population be in 2020?

   A 4,073,333   **B** 136,382   **C** 648,169   **D** 6.6×10^{12}

4. _____

5. A type of bacteria doubles in number every 25 minutes. Find the constant k for this type of bacteria, then write the equation for modeling this exponential growth.

5. _____

8 Chapter 8 Mid-Chapter Test

(Lessons 8-1 through 8-4)

SCORE _____

Assessment

Part I Write the letter for the correct answer in the blank at the right of each question.

1. Find the domain and range of the function shown.

   A $D = \{x \mid x > 0\}$, $R = \{$all real numbers$\}$

   B $D = \{$all real numbers$\}$, $R = \{y \mid y < 0\}$

   C $D = \{$all real numbers$\}$, $R = \{y \mid y > 0\}$

   D $D = \{x \mid x > 0\}$, $R = \{y \mid y > 0\}$

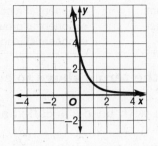

   1. _____

2. Solve $4^{2x} = 8^{x+4}$.

   F 2 **G** 6 **H** 12 **J** 24

   2. _____

3. Write the equation $4^3 = 64$ in logarithmic form.

   A $\log_3 4 = 64$ **C** $\log_{64} 3 = 4$

   B $\log_4 64 = 3$ **D** $\log_4 3 = 64$

   3. _____

4. Evaluate $\log_4 32$.

   F $\frac{5}{2}$ **G** 8 **H** 3 **J** $\frac{2}{5}$

   4. _____

5. Solve $\log_3 (7x - 3) \geq \log_3 (5x)$.

   A $\left\{x \mid x \geq \frac{3}{2}\right\}$ **B** $\left\{x \mid x > \frac{3}{7}\right\}$ **C** $\{x \mid x \geq 0\}$ **D** $\left\{x \mid x \geq \frac{2}{3}\right\}$

   5. _____

6. Write the equation $5^4 = 625$ in logarithmic form.

   F $\log_4 625 = 5$ **H** $\log_5 625 = 4$

   G $\log_4 5 = 625$ **J** $\log_5 4 = 625$

   6. _____

7. Write the equation $\log_7 49 = 2$ in exponential form.

   A $7^2 = 49$ **C** $49^2 = 7$

   B $49^7 = 2$ **D** $2^7 = 49$

   7. _____

8. Solve $\log_5 (2x - 1) > \log_5 (4x)$.

   F $\left\{x \mid x < \frac{1}{2}\right\}$ **H** $\left\{x \mid x > -\frac{1}{2}\right\}$

   G $\left\{x \mid x < -\frac{1}{2}\right\}$ **J** no solution

   8. _____

Part II

9. Write an exponential function whose graph passes through the points $(0, -3)$ and $(4, -48)$.

   9. _____

10. Write $\log_{\frac{1}{5}} m = -2$ in exponential form.

   10. _____

8 Chapter 8 Vocabulary Test

SCORE _____

asymptote	exponential decay	growth factor	natural base, e
Change of Base Formula	exponential equation	logarithm	natural base exponential
common logarithm	exponential function	logarithmic equation	function
compound interest	exponential growth	logarithmic function	natural logarithm
decay factor	exponential inequality	logarithmic inequality	

Choose from the terms above to complete each sentence.

1. A logarithm with base e is called a(n) _____.

2. The function $y = 10^x$ is an example of a(n) _____.

3. The equation $y = e^{-0.2t}$ is a model for _____.

4. The inverse of the function $y = e^x$ is the _____

5. The equation $y = 100(1 + 0.1)^t$ is a model for _____.

6. An exponential function with base e is called a(n) _____.

7. $y = \log_2 x$ is an example of a(n) _____.

8. $5^{x+1} = 125$ and $9^x = 27^{2x+1}$ are examples of _____.

9. A logarithm with base 10 is called a(n) _____.

10. In the equation $y = 20(1 + 0.02)^t$, $1 + 0.02$ is the _____.

Define each term in your own words.

11. logarithm

12. natural base, e

8 Chapter 8 Test, Form 1

SCORE _____

Assessment

Write the letter for the correct answer in the blank at the right of each question.

1. Find the domain and range of the function whose graph is shown.

   A $D = \{x \mid x > 0\}$; $R = \{y \mid y > 0\}$

   B $D = \{$all real numbers$\}$; $R = \{y \mid y > 0\}$

   C $D = \{x \mid x > 0\}$; $R = \{$all real numbers$\}$

   D $D = \{$all real numbers$\}$; $R = \{y \mid y < 0\}$

   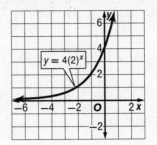

   1. _____

2. Which function represents exponential growth?

   F $y = 9\left(\frac{1}{3}\right)^x$ **G** $y = 4x^4$ **H** $y = 12\left(\frac{1}{5}\right)^x$ **J** $y = 10(3)^x$

   2. _____

3. The graph of which exponential function passes through the points $(0, 4)$ and $(1, 24)$?

   A $y = 4(6)^x$ **B** $y = 3(8)^x$ **C** $y = 2(2)^x$ **D** $y = 10(3)^x$

   3. _____

4. Solve $8^{x + 2} = 32^{2x + 4}$.

   F -2 **G** -1 **H** 0 **J** 1

   4. _____

5. Solve $2^{3m - 4} > 4$.

   A $\{x \mid m < 0\}$ **B** $\{x \mid m > 0\}$ **C** $\{x \mid m > 2\}$ **D** $\left\{x \mid m > \frac{5}{3}\right\}$

   5. _____

6. Write the equation $4^3 = 64$ in logarithmic form.

   F $\log_4 3 = 64$ **G** $\log_3 4 = 64$ **H** $\log_{64} 4 = 3$ **J** $\log_4 64 = 3$

   6. _____

7. Write the equation $\log_{12} 144 = 2$ in exponential form.

   A $144^2 = 12$ **B** $12^2 = 144$ **C** $2^{12} = 144$ **D** $144^{12} = 2$

   7. _____

8. Evaluate $\log_2 8$.

   F 3 **G** 4 **H** 16 **J** 64

   8. _____

9. Solve $\log_3 n = 2$.

   A 6 **B** 5 **C** 8 **D** 9

   9. _____

10. Solve $\log_2 2m > \log_2 (m + 5)$.

   F $\left\{x \mid m > \frac{5}{3}\right\}$ **G** $\{x \mid m < 5\}$ **H** $\{x \mid m > 5\}$ **J** $\{x \mid m > -5\}$

   10. _____

8   Chapter 8 Test, Form 1   *(continued)*

11. Use $\log_5 2 \approx 0.4307$ to approximate the value of $\log_5 4$.

    A 0.8614   **B** 0.8980   **C** 1.3652   **D** 0.1855   **11.** _____

12. Solve $\log_6 10 + \log_6 x = \log_6 40$.

    F 180   **G** 4   **H** 5   **J** 30   **12.** _____

13. Solve $4^x = 20$. Round to the nearest ten-thousandth.

    A 0.4628   **B** 1.5214   **C** 0.6990   **D** 2.1610   **13.** _____

14. Solve $3^x \geq 21$. Round to the nearest ten-thousandth.

    F $\{x \mid x \geq 0.8451\}$ **G** $\{x \mid x \geq 2.7712\}$ **H** $\{x \mid x \geq 0.3608\}$ **J** $\{x \mid x \geq 7.0000\}$ **14.** _____

15. Express $\log_9 22$ in terms of common logarithms.

    A $\log \dfrac{22}{9}$ **B** $\log 198$ **C** $\dfrac{\log 22}{\log 9}$ **D** $\dfrac{\log 9}{\log 22}$ **15.** _____

16. Evaluate $e^{\ln 4}$.

    F e^4 **G** 4^e **H** $\ln 4$ **J** 4   **16.** _____

17. Solve $e^x > 2.7$.

    A $\{x \mid x < 0.9933\}$ **B** $\{x \mid x > 0.9933\}$ **C** $\{x \mid x > 1.0668\}$ **D** $\{x \mid x < 1.0668\}$ **17.** _____

18. Solve $\ln 3x = 1$.

    F 20.0855   **G** 0.3333   **H** 0.9061   **J** 8.1548   **18.** _____

19. AUTOMOBILES Lydia bought a car for \$20,000. It is expected to depreciate at a continuous rate. What will be the value of the car in 2 years? Use $k = 0.105$ and round to the nearest dollar.

    A \$16,212   **B** \$16,012   **C** \$19,867   **D** \$18,567   **19.** _____

20. ART Martin bought a painting for \$5000. It is expected to appreciate at a continuous rate of 4%. How much will the painting be worth in 6 years? Round to the nearest cent.

    F \$6200.00   **G** \$5360.38   **H** \$37,647.68   **J** \$6356.25   **20.** _____

Bonus Evaluate $3 \log_2 64 + e^{\ln 5} + \log_{\frac{1}{3}} 9$.   **B:** _____

8 Chapter 8 Test, Form 2A   SCORE _____

Write the letter for the correct answer in the blank at the right of each question.

1. Find the domain and range of the function $y = 3\left(\frac{1}{5}\right)^x$.

   A D = {all real numbers}   **C** D = {x | x > 0}
      R = {y | y < 0}   R = {y | y > 0}

   B D = {all real numbers}   **D** D = {x | x > 0}
      R = {y | y > 0}   R = {all real numbers}   **1.** _____

2. Which function represents exponential *decay*?

   F $y = \frac{1}{100}(6)^x$ **G** $y = (4x)^{\frac{1}{2}}$ **H** $y = 2\left(\frac{4}{3}\right)^x$ **J** $y = 12\left(\frac{1}{8}\right)^x$ **2.** _____

3. Use the equation of the exponential function whose graph passes through the points (0, −3) and (2, −48) to find the value of y when x = −2.

   A $-\frac{3}{4}$ **B** $-\frac{3}{8}$ **C** $-\frac{3}{16}$ **D** 48   **3.** _____

4. Solve $4^{-2x + 7} = 32^{x - 8}$.

   F 0   **G** 2   **H** 4   **J** 6   **4.** _____

5. Solve $\left(\frac{1}{36}\right)^n = 216^{n + 5}$.

   A 10   **B** 3   **C** −3   **D** −10   **5.** _____

6. Solve $81^y < 27^{y + 3}$.

   F {x | y < −9}   **G** {x | y > 9}   **H** {x | y > −9}   **J** {x | y < 9}   **6.** _____

7. Write the equation $6561^{\frac{1}{4}} = 9$ in logarithmic form.

   A $\log_{\frac{1}{4}} 9 = 6561$ **C** $\log_9 6561 = \frac{1}{4}$

   B $\log_{6561} 9 = \frac{1}{4}$ **D** $\log_{\frac{1}{4}} 6561 = 9$ **7.** _____

8. Evaluate $5^{\log_5 63}$.

   F 58   **G** 315   **H** $\log_5 63$ **J** 63   **8.** _____

9. Solve $\log_{\frac{1}{5}} x = -1$.

   A $\frac{1}{25}$ **B** −5   **C** 5   **D** $-\frac{1}{5}$ **9.** _____

10. Solve $\log_3 (5x + 1) \geq \log_3 (3x + 7)$

   F {x | x ≥ 3}   **G** {x | x ≥ 4}   **H** {x | x ≤ 6}   **J** {x | x ≥ 27}   **10.** _____

Assessment

8 Chapter 8 Test, Form 2A *(continued)*

11. Use $\log_5 2 \approx 0.4307$ and $\log_5 3 \approx 0.6826$ to approximate the value of $\log_5 54$.

   A 0.1370   **B** 2.4785   **C** 0.8820   **D** 0.7488   **11.** _____

12. Solve $\log_4 (m - 3) + \log_4 (m + 3) = 2$.

   F $\sqrt{11}$ **G** 5   **H** 1   **J** −5.5   **12.** _____

13. Solve $6^{3n} = 43^{5n - 4}$. Round to the nearest ten-thousandth.

   A 1.1202   **B** −1.9005   **C** −0.2800   **D** 2.1418   **13.** _____

14. Solve $5^{2x + 1} \geq 50$. Round to the nearest ten-thousandth.

   F $\{x \,|\, x \geq 4.5000\}$ **G** $\{x \,|\, x \geq 0.7153\}$ **H** $\{x \,|\, x \geq 0\}$ **J** $\{x \,|\, x \geq 2.4307\}$ **14.** _____

15. Use common logarithms to approximate $\log_9 207$ to four decimal places.

   A 0.4120   **B** 1.3617   **C** 3.2702   **D** 2.4270   **15.** _____

16. Suppose you deposit \$1000 in an account paying 3% annual interest, compounded continuously. Use $A = Pe^{rt}$ to find the balance after 10 years.

   F \$20,085.54   **G** \$1300   **H** \$1349.86   **J** \$1068.65   **16.** _____

17. Solve $4 + 3e^{5x} = 27$.

   A 0.4074   **B** 0.4394   **C** 2.0369   **D** 0.1769   **17.** _____

18. Solve $\ln (x + 5) \geq 2$.

   F $\{x \,|\, x \geq 2.3891\}$ **G** $\{x \,|\, x \leq 2.3891\}$ **H** $\{x \,|\, x \geq 12.3891\}$ **J** $\{x \,|\, x \leq 12.3891\}$ **18.** _____

19. CHEMISTRY A particular compound decays according to the equation $y = ae^{-0.0974t}$, where t is in days. Find the half-life of this compound.

   A about 5.1 days   **C** about 7.1 days

   B about 7.4 days   **D** about 9.7 days   **19.** _____

20. TOURISM At a town with a large convention center, the cost of a hotel room has increased 5.1% annually. If the average hotel room cost \$48.00 in 1980 and this growth continues, what will an average hotel room cost in 2012? Use $y = a(1 + r)^t$ and round to the nearest cent.

   F \$143.38   **G** \$235.79   **H** \$126.34   **J** \$87.19   **20.** _____

Bonus Solve $5^{\log_5 2x - \log_5 (x - 3)} = \ln e^{x + 4}$.   **B:** _____

8 Chapter 8 Test, Form 2B

SCORE _____

Copyright © Glencoe/McGraw-Hill, a division of The McGraw-Hill Companies, Inc.

Assessment

Write the letter for the correct answer in the blank at the right of each question.

1. Find the domain and range of the function $y = \frac{1}{2}(2)^x$.

   A D = {all real numbers} **C** D = {x | x > 0}
      R = {y | y > 0}   R = {y | y > 0}

   B D = {all real numbers} **D** D = {x | x > 0}
      R = {y | y < 0}   R = {all real numbers}

   1. _____

2. Which function represents exponential *growth*?

   F $y = \frac{1}{20}\left(\frac{5}{2}\right)^x$ **G** $y = 16(0.4)^x$ **H** $y = 20\left(\frac{1}{8}\right)^x$ **J** $y = 8x^3$

   2. _____

3. Use the equation of the exponential function whose graph passes through the points $(0, -2)$ and $(2, -50)$ to find the value of y when $x = -2$.

   A $-\frac{1}{100}$ **B** 50   **C** $-\frac{2}{25}$ **D** $-\frac{1}{50}$

   3. _____

4. Solve $4^{2x + 7} = 32^{x + 3}$.

   F -2 **G** -1 **H** 1   **J** 2

   4. _____

5. Solve $\left(\frac{1}{81}\right)^t = 243^{t - 2}$.

   A $\frac{9}{2}$ **B** $\frac{10}{9}$ **C** $\frac{2}{9}$ **D** $\frac{9}{10}$

   5. _____

6. Solve $64^x < 32^{x + 2}$.

   F $\{x \mid x > -10\}$ **G** $\{x \mid x < -10\}$ **H** $\{x \mid x > 10\}$ **J** $\{x \mid x < 10\}$

   6. _____

7. Write the equation $\log_{243} 81 = \frac{4}{5}$ in exponential form.

   A $81^{\frac{4}{5}} = 243$ **B** $243^{\frac{4}{5}} = 81$ **C** $\left(\frac{4}{5}\right)^{81} = 243$ **D** $\left(\frac{4}{5}\right)^{243} = 81$

   7. _____

8. Evaluate $9^{\log_9 54}$.

   F $\log_9 54$ **G** 54   **H** 6   **J** 486

   8. _____

9. Solve $\log_{\frac{1}{8}} x = -1$.

   A 8   **B** -8 **C** 0   **D** $-\frac{1}{8}$

   9. _____

10. Solve $\log_2 (7x - 3) \geq \log_2 (x + 12)$.

    F $\left\{x \mid x \leq \frac{5}{2}\right\}$ **G** $\left\{x \mid x \leq -\frac{5}{2}\right\}$ **H** $\left\{x \mid x \geq \frac{3}{2}\right\}$ **J** $\left\{x \mid x \geq \frac{5}{2}\right\}$

    10. _____

8   Chapter 8 Test, Form 2B   *(continued)*

11. Use $\log_5 2 \approx 0.4307$ and $\log_5 3 \approx 0.6826$ to approximate the value of $\log_5 12$.

   A 0.8681   **B** 0.1266   **C** 1.5440   **D** 0.5880   **11.** _____

12. Solve $\log_3 ct + \log_3 (a - 8) = 2$.

   F 8   **G** 5   **H** 9   **J** −1, 9   **12.** _____

13. Solve $9^{2n} = 40^{4n - 7}$. Round to the nearest ten-thousandth.

   A 2.4922   **B** 0.4012   **C** −0.3560   **D** 4.7209   **13.** _____

14. Solve $3^{5x - 1} \le 30$. Round to the nearest ten-thousandth.

   F $\{x \mid x \le 0.4000\}$ **G** $\{x \mid x \le 0.8192\}$ **H** $\{x \mid x \le 1.8000\}$ **J** $\{x \mid x \le 3.0959\}$ **14.** _____

15. Use common logarithms to approximate $\log_9 72$ to four decimal places.

   A −0.3427   **B** 0.9692   **C** 1.9464   **D** 2.2411   **15.** _____

16. Suppose you deposit \$1000 in an account paying 4% annual interest, compounded continuously. Use $A = Pe^{rt}$ to find the balance after 10 years.

   F \$1491.82   **G** \$5459.82   **H** \$1040.81   **J** \$2353.85   **16.** _____

17. Solve $\ln (x + 2) = 3$.

   A 22.0855   **B** 18.0855   **C** 20.0855   **D** −0.9014   **17.** _____

18. Solve $e^{-9x} \le 6$.

   F $\{x \mid x \ge -1.8122\}$ **G** $\{x \mid x \ge -0.08646\}$

   H $\{x \mid x \ge 1.7918\}$ **J** $\{x \mid x \ge -0.1991\}$ **18.** _____

19. CHEMISTRY A particular compound decays according to the equation $y = ae^{-0.0736t}$, where t is in days. Find the half-life of this compound.

   A about 9.1 days   **C** about 6.8 days

   B about 9.4 days   **D** about 7.4 days   **19.** _____

20. FOOD PRICES At a wholesale food distribution center, the price of sugar has increased 6.3% annually since 1980. Suppose sugar cost \$0.43 per pound in 1980 and this growth continues. What will a pound of sugar cost in 2017? Use $y = a(1 + r)t$ and round to the nearest cent.

   F \$4.12   **G** \$1.21   **H** \$2.42   **J** \$3.30   **20.** _____

Bonus Solve $2^{\log_2 5x - \log_2 (x + 1)} = \ln e^x$.   **B:** _____

8   Chapter 8 Test, Form 2C

SCORE _____

Assessment

1. Sketch the graph of $y = \left(\frac{1}{2}\right)(3)^x$. Then state the function's domain and range.

1.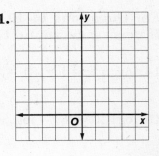

_____

2. Determine whether the function $y = 0.8\left(\frac{2}{3}\right)^x$ represents exponential *growth* or *decay*.

2. _____

3. Write an exponential function whose graph passes through the points $(0, -6)$ and $(-2, -54)$.

3. _____

4. Solve $9^{4x + 4} = 243^{2x + 2}$.

4. _____

5. Solve $\frac{1}{6} = 6^{n + 4}$.

5. _____

6. Solve $32^x < 16^{x + 2}$.

6. _____

7. Write the equation $\log_{81} \frac{1}{9} = -\frac{1}{2}$ in exponential form.

7. _____

8. Evaluate $\log_9 9^7$.

8. _____

9. Evaluate $\log_4 128$.

9. _____

10. Solve $\log_{36} n = \frac{3}{2}$.

10. _____

11. Solve $\log_5 (8x) > \log_5 (3x + 10)$.

11. _____

Use $\log_5 2 \approx 0.4307$ and $\log_5 3 \approx 0.6826$ to approximate the value of each expression.

12. $\log_5 48$

12. _____

13. $\log_5 \frac{5}{3}$

13. _____

8 Chapter 8 Test, Form 2C (continued)

**For Questions 14–19, solve each equation or inequality.
If necessary, round to the nearest ten-thousandth.**

14. $\log_4 n = \frac{1}{4} \log_4 81 + \frac{1}{2} \log_4 25$

14. _____

15. $\log_2 (2x + 6) - \log_2 x = 3$

15. _____

16. $\log_3 (x + 3) + \log_3 (x - 2) = \log_3 14$

16. _____

17. $6^{n-2} = 50$

17. _____

18. $2^y = 5^{y-2}$

18. _____

19. $4^{3x+1} < 28$

19. _____

20. Express $\log_{12} 4$ in terms of common logarithms. Then
approximate its value to the nearest ten-thousandth.

20. _____

21. Suppose you deposit \$3000 in an account paying 2% annual
interest, compounded continuously. Use $A = Pe^{rt}$ to find the
balance after 5 years.

21. _____

22. Solve $\ln (x - 5) = 3$.

22. _____

23. Solve $e^{-4x} \leq 9$.

23. _____

24. **CHEMISTRY** After 12 hours, half of a 16-gram sample of a
radioactive element remains. Find the constant k for this
element for t hours, then write the equation for modeling its
exponential decay.

24. _____

25. **SAVINGS** A savings account deposit of \$150 is to earn 6.5%
interest. After how many years will the investment be worth
\$450? Use $y = a(1 + r)^t$ and round to the nearest tenth.

25. _____

Bonus Evaluate $(\log_4 12^3)(\log_{12} 4^3)$.

B: _____

8   Chapter 8 Test, Form 2D   SCORE _____

1. Sketch the graph of $y = 6\left(\frac{1}{2}\right)^x$. Then state the function's domain and range.

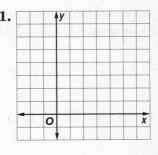

1. _____

_____

2. Determine whether the function $y = 0.3\left(\frac{8}{5}\right)^x$ represents exponential *growth* or *decay*.

2. _____

3. Write an exponential function whose graph passes through the points $(0, -5)$ and $(-3, -40)$.

3. _____

4. Solve $9^{3x + 4} = 243^{x + 2}$.

4. _____

5. Solve $\left(\frac{1}{4}\right)^{m - 7} = 16$.

5. _____

6. Solve $10^{x + 3} > 100^{x - 1}$.

6. _____

7. Write the equation $5^{-4} = \frac{1}{625}$ in logarithmic form.

7. _____

8. Evaluate $\log_6 6^8$.

8. _____

9. Evaluate $\log_8 128$.

9. _____

10. Solve $\log_{64} x = \frac{2}{3}$.

10. _____

11. Solve $\log_4 (2x + 5) \leq \log_4 (3x - 2)$.

11. _____

Use $\log_5 2 \approx 0.4307$ and $\log_5 3 \approx 0.6826$ to approximate the value of each expression.

12. $\log_5 18$

12. _____

13. $\log_5 \frac{5}{2}$

13. _____

8 Chapter 8 Test, Form 2D *(continued)*

For Questions 14–19, solve each equation or inequality. If necessary, round to the nearest ten-thousandth.

14. $\log_5 n = \frac{1}{3} \log_5 64 + \frac{1}{2} \log_5 49$

14. _____

15. $\log_6 (5 - 2a) - \log_6 (3a) = 1$

15. _____

16. $\log_3 (x - 3) + \log_3 (x + 2) = \log_3 6$

16. _____

17. $7^{n + 3} = 80$

17. _____

18. $3^n = 6^{n - 2}$

18. _____

19. $5^{4x - 1} < 30$

19. _____

20. Express $\log_{15} 5$ in terms of common logarithms. Then approximate its value to the nearest ten-thousandth.

20. _____

21. Suppose you deposit $500 in an account paying 4% annual interest, compounded continuously. Use $A = Pe^{rt}$ to find the balance after 5 years.

21. _____

22. Solve $\ln (x + 4) = 4$.

22. _____

23. Solve $e^{-3x} \leq 18$.

23. _____

24. CHEMISTRY In 5 years, radioactivity reduces the mass of a 100-gram sample of an element to 75 grams. Find the constant k for this element for t in years, then write the equation for modeling this exponential decay.

24. _____

25. SAVINGS A savings account deposit of $300 is to earn 5.8% interest. After how many years will the investment be worth $900? Use $y = a(1 + r)^t$ and round to the nearest tenth.

25. _____

Bonus Evaluate $(\log_5 20^4)(\log_{20} 5^4)$.

B: _____

8   **Chapter 8 Test, Form 3**   SCORE _____

1. Sketch the graph of $y = -1.5(4)^x$. Then state the function's domain and range.

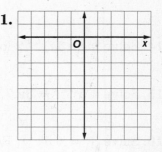

1. _____

2. Determine whether the function $y = 0.4(3.8)^{-x}$ represents exponential *growth* or *decay*.

    2. _____

3. Write an exponential function whose graph passes through $(0, -0.3)$ and $(2, -10.8)$

    3. _____

4. Solve $2^{4x} \cdot 32^{1-x} = 8^{x+2}$.

    4. _____

5. Solve $\left(\dfrac{1}{81}\right)^{4m+1} \geq \left(\dfrac{1}{27}\right)^{5m}$.

    5. _____

6. Evaluate $2^{\log_2 (8x-1)}$.

    6. _____

7. Evaluate $\log_3 243^x$.

    7. _____

8. Solve $\log_x [\log_2 (\log_3 9)] = 2$.

    8. _____

9. Solve $\log_3 (a^2 - 12) > \log_3 a$.

    9. _____

For Questions 10 and 11, use $\log_5 2 \approx 0.4307$ and $\log_5 3 \approx 0.6826$ to approximate the value of each expression.

10. $\log_5 \dfrac{15}{4}$

    10. _____

11. $\log_5 1.2$

    11. _____

12. Solve $\log_4 0.25 + 3 \log_4 x = 5 \log_4 2 + \dfrac{1}{3} \log_4 64$.

    12. _____

13. Solve $\log_4 (4b + 14) - \log_4 (b^2 - 3b - 17) = \dfrac{1}{2}$.

    13. _____

Assessment

8   Chapter 8 Test, Form 3   *(continued)*

14. Solve $\log_a (3n) > 2 \log_a x = \log_a x$ for n.

14. _____

15. Solve $4.5^{x^2 + 2} = 32.7$. Round to the nearest ten-thousandth.

15. _____

16. Solve $3^n = \sqrt{5^{n-2}}$. Round to the nearest ten-thousandth.

16. _____

17. Solve $\left(\frac{1}{2}\right)^{2t} > 5^{3-4t}$. Round to the nearest ten-thousandth.

17. _____

18. Express $\log_5 (2.1)^3$ in terms of common logarithms. Then approximate its value to the nearest ten-thousandth.

18. _____

19. Evaluate $e^{4 \ln x}$.

19. _____

20. Solve $\ln (x + 3) + \ln x = \ln 4$.

20. _____

21. Solve $\ln (x^2 + 10) > \ln x + \ln 7$.

21. _____

For Questions 22 and 23, use the following information.

The population of Suffolk County in Massachusetts decreased from 663,906 in 1990 to 641,695 in 1999.

22. Write an exponential decay equation of the form $y = ae^{kt}$ for Suffolk County, where t is the number of years after 1990.

22. _____

23. Use your equation to predict the population of Suffolk County in 2020.

23. _____

24. HOME OWNERSHIP The Richardson family bought a house 12 years ago for $95,000. The house is now worth $167,000. Assuming a steady rate of growth, what was the yearly rate of appreciation?

24. _____

25. SCHOOL ENROLLMENT At a certain school, the number of children entering kindergarten increased by 6.7% annually for 5 years and then decreased by 4.2% annually in the next 5 years. If 110 children enrolled in kindergarten at the beginning of this period, how many were enrolled after 10 years?

25. _____

Bonus Solve $\log x^2 = (\log x)^2$.

B: _____

8 Chapter 8 Extended-Response Test

SCORE _____

Demonstrate your knowledge by giving a clear, concise solution to each problem. Be sure to include all relevant drawings and justify your answers. You may show your solutions in more than one way or investigate beyond the requirements of the problem.

1. For the equation $y = ab^x$, where $a > 0$, we know that if $b > 1$, the function represents exponential growth, while it represents exponential decay if $0 < b < 1$.

   a. Choose a positive value for a and let $b = 1$. Complete the table for these values of a and b. Is $y = ab^x$ an exponential function? Explain your reasoning.

x	−3	−2	−1	0	1	2	3
$y = ab^x$							

   b. Choose a positive value for a and a negative value for b. Complete the table for these values. Is $y = ab^x$ an exponential function? Explain your reasoning.

x	−3	−2	−1	0	1	2	3
$y = ab^x$							

2. **a.** Solve the exponential equation $3^{5x} = 9^{x+6}$ by rewriting the equation so that each side has the same base.

   b. Solve the equation in part **a** using common logarithms.

   c. Which method do you prefer? Explain your reasoning.

   d. Write and solve an exponential equation that you would also prefer to solve using the method you chose in part **c**.

3. **a.** How are the three equations below alike? How are they different?
   $$\log_3 x = 2 \qquad \log x = 2 \qquad \ln x = 2$$

   b. Solve each equation in part **a** above. Then write and solve a fourth equation that shares the same similarities and differences as the three given equations.

4. Ruby solved the exponential inequality $2^{2z} \geq 12^{z+1}$ and stated that the solution set was $\{z \mid z \geq 22.2619\}$. When she checked her solution however, Ruby found that $z = 1$, which is in her solution set, does *not* make the original inequality true. When she checked $z = -3$, which is *not* in her solution set, the original inequality *is* true.

   a. Show how Ruby arrived at her solution using common logarithms.

   b. What do her checks of $z = 1$ and $z = -3$ indicate about Ruby's solution?

   c. What change must be made to the solution and why must that change be made?

5. **ECONOMICS** The Jones Corporation found that its annual profit could be modeled by the exponential equation $y = 10(0.99)^t$, while the Davis Company's annual profit is modeled by $y = 8(1.01)^t$. For both equations, profit is given in millions of dollars, and t is the number of years since 1990.

   a. Find each company's annual profit for the years between 1990 and 2000 to the nearest dollar.

   b. In which company would you prefer to own stock? Explain your reasoning.

   c. Indicate how a comparison of the two profit equations would support your decision.

Assessment

SCORE _____

8 Standardized Test Practice

(Chapters 1–8)

Part 1: Multiple Choice

Instructions: Fill in the appropriate circle for the best answer.

---

1. If $\frac{x}{8} > x$, which could be a value for x?

   A -1 **B** 0 **C** 2 **D** $\frac{1}{4}$

   1. Ⓐ Ⓑ Ⓒ Ⓓ

2. If $0 < a < 1$, which of the following increases as a decreases?

   F $a - 1$ **G** $a^2 - 1$ **H** $\frac{1}{a}$ **J** a^2

   2. Ⓕ Ⓖ Ⓗ Ⓙ

3. If $3x - 2$ is an odd integer, what is the next consecutive odd integer?

   A $3x - 1$ **B** $3x - 3$ **C** $3x + 1$ **D** $3x$

   3. Ⓐ Ⓑ Ⓒ Ⓓ

4. Jody sold 4 more than twice the number of cars that Laura sold. If Laura sold c cars, how many more did Jody sell than Laura?

   F 4 **G** $c + 4$ **H** $3c + 4$ **J** $2c + 4$

   4. Ⓕ Ⓖ Ⓗ Ⓙ

5. If $8 - 3z = 16 + 5z$, then what is the value of $4z$?

   A -16 **B** -4 **C** 1 **D** 12

   5. Ⓐ Ⓑ Ⓒ Ⓓ

6. The radius of a wheel is 6 inches. How many revolutions will it make if it is rolled a distance of 288π inches?

   F 8 **G** 8π **H** 24 **J** 24π

   6. Ⓕ Ⓖ Ⓗ Ⓙ

7. What is the 8th term in the sequence 3, 2, 0, -4, -12, …?

   A -124 **B** -60 **C** -36 **D** -144

   7. Ⓐ Ⓑ Ⓒ Ⓓ

8. Which Venn diagram models the relationships among the sets $A = \{1, 2, 3\}$, $B = \{-4, 0\}$, and $C = \{$positive integers$\}$?

   F   **G**   **H**   **J**

   8. Ⓕ Ⓖ Ⓗ Ⓙ

9. A total of \$270 is to be divided among four children. Each will receive an amount that is proportional to his or her age. If the children are 5, 10, 14, and 16 years old, how much money does the youngest child receive?

   A \$96   **B** \$6   **C** \$30   **D** \$54

   9. Ⓐ Ⓑ Ⓒ Ⓓ

10. If $m^2 + n^2 = 140$ and $mn = 49$, what is the value of $(m - n)^2$?

   F 0 **G** 24 **H** 238 **J** 42

   10. Ⓕ Ⓖ Ⓗ Ⓙ

8 Standardized Test Practice *(continued)*

11. What is the slope of a line that is perpendicular to the graph of $5x + 4y = 7$?

A $-\dfrac{5}{4}$ **B** $\dfrac{5}{4}$ **C** $-\dfrac{4}{5}$ **D** $\dfrac{4}{5}$ 11. Ⓐ Ⓑ Ⓒ Ⓓ

12. The graph of which equation is a line with undefined slope that passes through $(5, 1)$?

F $y = 1$ **G** $y = 5$ **H** $x = 1$ **J** $x = 5$ 12. Ⓕ Ⓖ Ⓗ Ⓙ

13. Which point does not satisfy the inequality $y < |2x - 3|$?

A $(0, 2)$ **B** $(-1, -3)$ **C** $(1, 3)$ **D** $(2, 0)$ 13. Ⓐ Ⓑ Ⓒ Ⓓ

14. To solve the system of equations $3x - y = 5$ and $2x + 3y = 18$, which expression could be substituted for y into the second equation?

F $5 - 3x$ **G** $3x - 5$ **H** $6 - \dfrac{2}{3}x$ **J** $18 - 2x$ 14. Ⓕ Ⓖ Ⓗ Ⓙ

Part 2: Gridded Response

Instructions: Enter your answer by writing each digit of the answer in a column box and then shading in the appropriate circle that corresponds to that entry.

15. If $\ell \parallel m$ in the figure shown, what is the value of d?

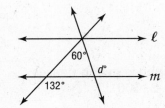

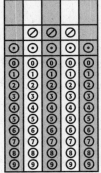

15.

16. Find the perimeter of square *EFGH* if the areas of rectangle *ABCD* and square *EFGH* are equal.

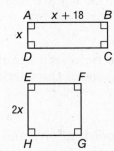

16.

Assessment

8 Standardized Test Practice (continued)

Part 3: Short Response

Instructions: Write your answers in the space provided.

17. Solve $2x^2 = x + 1$ by graphing. If exact roots cannot be found, state the consecutive integers between which the roots are located.

17.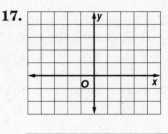

_____

18. Find $(f + g)(x)$, $(f - g)(x)$, $(f \cdot g)(x)$, and $\left(\dfrac{f}{g}\right)(x)$ for $f(x) = x^2 + 2x - 15$ and $g(x) = 2x - 1$.

18. _____

For Questions 19 and 20, simplify.

19. $\dfrac{10mp^4}{r^2} \div \left(\dfrac{5mp}{r^3}\right)^2$

19. _____

20. $\dfrac{4}{x - 5} - \dfrac{3}{5 - x}$

20. _____

21. Write an exponential function whose graph passes through the points $(0, 4)$ and $(-2, 100)$.

21. _____

22. A new camp site will contain t tent sites, with 25 square meters of land each, and r recreational vehicle (RV) sites with 40 square meters of land each. No more than 90 camp sites can be built on the 3000 square meters of land available.

a. Write a system of inequalities to represent the number of sites built. Then list the coordinates of the vertices of the feasible region.

22a. _____

b. The site owner will charge $14 per tent site and $20 per RV site per day. Write a function for the total profit per day.

b. _____

c. Determine the number of each type of site needed to earn a maximum profit, and find the maximum profit per day.

c. _____

NAME _____ DATE _____ PERIOD _____

8-1 Study Guide and Intervention

Graphing Exponential Functions

Exponential Growth An exponential growth function has the form $y = b^x$, where $b > 1$. The graphs of exponential equations can be transformed by changing the value of the constants a, h, and k in the exponential equation: $f(x) = ab^{x-h} + k$.

Parent Function of Exponential Growth Functions, $f(x) = b^x$, $b > 1$
1. The function is continuous, one-to-one, and increasing.
2. The domain is the set of all real numbers.
3. The x-axis is the asymptote of the graph.
4. The range is the set of all non-zero real numbers.
5. The graph contains the point (0, 1).

Example   Graph $y = 4^x + 2$. State the domain and range.

Make a table of values. Connect the points to form a smooth curve.

x	−1	0	1	2	3
y	2.25	3	6	18	66

The domain of the function is all real numbers, while the range is the set of all positive real numbers greater than 2.

Exercises

Graph each function. State the domain and range.

1. $y = 3(2)^x$

2. $y = \frac{1}{3}(3)^x$

3. $y = 0.25(5)^x$

D = {all real numbers};
R = {y|y > 0}

4. $y = 2(3)^x$

5. $y = 4^x - 2$

6. $y = 2^{x+5}$

D = {all real numbers};
R = {y|y > 0}

D = {all real numbers};
R = {y|y > −2}

D = {all real numbers};
R = {y|y > 0}

NAME _____ DATE _____ PERIOD _____

8 Anticipation Guide

Exponential and Logarithmic Functions and Relations

Step 1   *Before you begin Chapter 8*

- Read each statement.
- Decide whether you Agree (A) or Disagree (D) with the statement.
- Write A or D in the first column OR if you are not sure whether you agree or disagree, write NS (Not Sure).

STEP 1 A, D, or NS	Statement	STEP 2 A or D
	1. The graph of any exponential function is continuous.	A
	2. In the exponential function $y = ab^x$, if a is negative then y represents exponential decay.	D
	3. If $21^x > 21^3$, then $x > 3$.	A
	4. The inverse of $y = b^x$ is $y = \left(\frac{1}{b}\right)^x$.	D
	5. $3^2 = 9$ in logarithmic form is $\log_2 3 = 9$.	D
	6. If $\log_3(2x) = \log_3(x^2 + 1)$, then $2x = x^2 + 1$.	A
	7. The logarithm of a product is the product of the logarithms of its factors.	D
	8. $4\log_5 9$ is equal to $\log_5 9^4$.	A
	9. Common logarithms are logarithms with a base of 2, 5, or 10.	D
	10. A natural logarithm is a logarithm with base e.	A
	11. Exponential decay is when a quantity decreases by a fixed amount during a certain period of time.	D
	12. The percent of increase in an exponential growth problem is called the *rate of growth*.	A

Step 2   *After you complete Chapter 8*

- Reread each statement and complete the last column by entering an A or a D.
- Did any of your opinions about the statements change from the first column?
- For those statements that you mark with a D, use a piece of paper to write an example of why you disagree.

Top worksheet (Skills Practice)

NAME _____ DATE _____ PERIOD _____

8-1 Skills Practice

Graphing Exponential Functions

Graph each function. State the function's domain and range.

1. $y = 3(2)^x$

$D = \{\text{all real numbers}\}$,
$R = \{y \mid y > 0\}$

2. $y = 2\left(\frac{1}{2}\right)^x$

D = {all real numbers},
R = {y | y > 0}

3. $y = -\frac{3}{2}(1.5)^x$

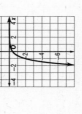

$D = \{\text{all real numbers}\}$,
$R = \{y \mid y < 0\}$

4. $y = 3\left(\frac{1}{3}\right)^x$

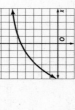

D = {all real numbers},
R = {y | y > 0}

For each graph $f(x)$ is the parent function and $g(x)$ is a transformation of $f(x)$. Use the graph to determine $g(x)$.

5. $f(x) = 4^x$

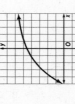

$g(x) = -4^x$

6. $f(x) = \left(\frac{1}{5}\right)^x$

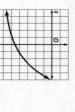

$g(x) = -\left(\frac{1}{5}\right)^{x+2}$

Chapter 8   7   *Glencoe Algebra 2*

Bottom worksheet (Study Guide and Intervention)

NAME _____ DATE _____ PERIOD _____

8-1 Study Guide and Intervention *(continued)*

Graphing Exponential Functions

Exponential Decay The following table summarizes the characteristics of exponential decay functions.

Parent Function of Exponential Decay Functions, $f(x) = b^x$, $0 < b < 1$	1. The function is continuous, one-to-one, and decreasing.
	2. The domain is the set of all real numbers.
	3. The x-axis is the asymptote of the graph.
	4. The range is the set of all positive real numbers.
	5. The graph contains the point (0, 1).

Example   Graph $y = \left(\frac{1}{2}\right)^x$. State the domain and range.

Make a table of values. Connect the points to form a smooth curve. The domain is all real numbers and the range is the set of all positive real numbers.

x	−2	−1	0	1	2
y	4	2	1	0.5	0.25

Exercises

Graph each function. State the domain and range.

1. $y = 6\left(\frac{1}{2}\right)^x$

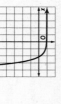

D = {all real numbers};
R = {y|y > 0}

2. $y = -2\left(\frac{1}{4}\right)^x$

D = {all real numbers};
R = {y|y < 0}

3. $y = -0.4(0.2)^x$

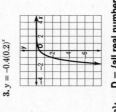

D = {all real numbers};
R = {y|y < 0}

4. $y = \left(\frac{2}{5}\right)\left(\frac{1}{2}\right)^{x-1} + 2$

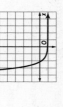

D = {all real numbers};
R = {y|y > 2}

5. $y = 4\left(\frac{1}{5}\right)^{x+3} - 1$

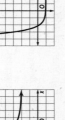

D = {all real numbers};
R = {y|y > −1}

6. $y = \left(-\frac{1}{3}\right)\left(\frac{3}{4}\right)^{x-5} + 6$

D = {all real numbers};
R = {y|y < 6}

Chapter 8   6   *Glencoe Algebra 2*

Lesson 8-1

NAME _____ DATE _____ PERIOD _____

8-1 Word Problem Practice

Graphing Exponential Functions

1. **GOLF BALLS** A golf ball manufacturer packs 3 golf balls into a single package. Three of these packages make a gift box. Three gift boxes make a value pack. The display shelf is high enough to stack 3 value packs one on top of the other. Three such columns of value packs make up a display front. Three display fronts can be packed in a single shipping box and shipped to various retail stores. How many golf balls are in a single shipping box? **729**

2. **FOLDING** Paper thickness ranges from 0.0032 inch to 0.0175 inch. Kay folds a piece of paper 0.01 inch thick in half over and over until it is at least 25 layers thick. How many times does she fold the paper in half and how many layers are there? How thick is the folded paper? **5 folds; 32 layers; 0.32 in.**

3. **SUBSCRIPTIONS** Subscriptions to an online arts and crafts club have been increasing by 20% every year. The club began with 40 members.

Year	0	1	2	3	4
Subscriptions	40	48			

Make a graph of the number of subscribers over the first 5 years of the club's existence.

4. **TENNIS SHOES** The cost of a pair of tennis shoes increases about 5.1% every year. About how much would a $50 pair of tennis shoes cost 25 years from now? **$173.40**

5. **MONEY** Sam opened a savings account that compounds interest at a rate of 3% annually. Let P be the initial amount Sam deposited and let t be the number of years the account has been open.

a. Write an equation to find A, the amount of money in the account after t years. Assume that Sam made more additional deposits and no withdrawals. $A = P(1.03)^t$

b. If Sam opened the account with $500 and made no deposits or withdrawals, how much is in the account 10 years later? **$671.96**

c. What is the least number of years it would take for such an account to double in value? **24 yr**

NAME _____ DATE _____ PERIOD _____

8-1 Practice

Graphing Exponential Functions

Graph each function. State the domain and range.

1. $y = 1.5(2)^x$

D = {all real numbers};
R = {y|y > 0}

2. $y = 4(3)^x$

D = {all real numbers};
R = {y|y > 0}

3. $y = 3(0.5)^x$

D = {all real numbers};
R = {y|y > 0}

4. $y = 5\left(\frac{1}{2}\right)^x - 8$

D = {all real numbers};
R = {y|y > -8}

5. $y = -2\left(\frac{1}{4}\right)^{x-3}$

D = {all real numbers};
R = {y|y < 0}

6. $y = \frac{1}{2}(3)^{x+4} - 5$

D = {all real numbers};
R = {y|y > -5}

7. **BIOLOGY** The initial number of bacteria in a culture is 12,000. The culture doubles each day.

a. Write an exponential function to model the population y of bacteria after x days. $y = 12,000(2)^x$

b. How many bacteria are there after 6 days? **768,000**

8. **EDUCATION** A college with a graduating class of 4000 students in the year 2008 predicts that its graduating class will grow 5% per year. Write an exponential function to model the number of students y in the graduating class t years after 2008. $y = 4000(1.05)^t$

Answers (Lesson 8-1)

NAME _____ DATE _____ PERIOD _____

8-1 Graphing Calculator Activity

Regression Equation Lab

A graphing calculator can be used to determine a regression equation that best fits a set of data. This activity requires tiles labeled on one side, and a container.

Collect the Data

Step 1 Place the tiles on the desktop and count the total number. Record the total number. Then place the tiles in the container and gently shake.

Step 2 Pour the tiles onto the desktop, remove all the tiles with a label showing, and set these aside. Count the remaining tiles without the labels showing and return them to the container.

Step 3 Record the data in a table like this one.

Trials	Number of tiles without label showing	
x	y	
1		
2		

Step 4 Repeat step 2 and 3 until the number of tiles without labels is zero or the number remains constant.

Step 5 Take the tiles that were set aside in Step 2 and pour them out of the container onto the desktop. Remove the tiles without the label showing and count the tiles with the label showing. Repeat this process until all the tiles have been removed.

Step 6 Record the data in a table like this one.

Trials	Number of tiles without label showing	
x	y	
1		
2		

Analyze the Data

1–6. Answers will vary.

1. Use [STAT] to enter trials in **L1** and number of tiles without label showing in **L2**. Enter trials in **L3** and number of tiles with the label showing in **L4**.

2. Use [STATPLOT] to make a scatter plot. Make a graph on paper for each plot. Record the window used. Describe the pattern of the points.

3. From the [STAT] [CALC] menu find the regression equation that best fits the data. Record the two closest equations, rounding values to the nearest hundredths. List and discuss the r and/or r^2 values. Also include the graphs in determining the best-fitting regression equation.

4. Sketch your best-fit regression equation choice for each scatter-plot on paper.

5. Describe any problems with the data or the regression equations.

6. Insert (0, total number of tiles) in the tables and the lists. Describe the effect on the graphs. What happens with [PwrReg] and [ExpReg] when this ordered pair is inserted? Explain why this occurs.

NAME _____ DATE _____ PERIOD _____

8-1 Enrichment

Families of Curves

Use these graphs for the problems below.

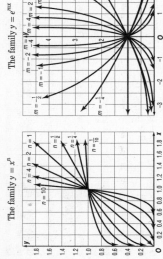

The family $y = x^n$

The family $y = e^{mx}$

1. Use the graph on the left to describe the relationship among the curves $y = x^{\frac{1}{2}}, y = x^1,$ and $y = x^2.$ **For $n = \frac{1}{2}$ and $n = 2,$ the graphs are reflections of one another in the line with equation $y = x^1.$**

2. Graph $y = x^n$ for $n = \frac{1}{10}, \frac{1}{4},$ and 10 on the grid with $y = x^{\frac{1}{2}}, y = x^1,$ and $y = x^2.$ **See students' graphs.**

3. Which two regions in the first quadrant contain no points of the graphs of the family for $y = x^n$?
$$\{(x, y)|x \geq 1 \text{ and } 0 < y \leq 1\} \text{ and } \{(x, y)|0 < x \leq 1 \text{ and } y \geq 1\}$$

4. On the right grid, graph the members of the family $y = e^{mx}$ for which $m = 1$ and $m = -1.$ The number e is irrational. It is about 2.71828. Use a calculator to evaluate the function and complete the graphs. **See students' graphs.**

5. Describe the relationship among these two curves and the y-axis. **The graphs for $m = 1$ and $m = -1$ are reflections in the y-axis.**

6. Graph $y = e^{mx}$ for $m = 0, \pm\frac{1}{4}, \pm\frac{1}{2}, \pm2,$ and $\pm4.$ **See students' graphs.**

NAME _____ DATE _____ PERIOD _____

8-2 Study Guide and Intervention (continued)

Solve Exponential Equations and Inequalities

Solve Exponential Inequalities An exponential inequality is an inequality involving exponential functions.

Property of Inequality for Exponential Functions	If $b > 1$ then $b^x > b^y$ if and only if $x > y$ and $b^x < b^y$ if and only if $x < y$.

Example Solve $5^{2x-1} > \frac{1}{125}$.

$5^{2x-1} > \frac{1}{125}$	Original inequality
$5^{2x-1} > 5^{-3}$	Rewrite $\frac{1}{125}$ as 5^{-3}
$2x - 1 > -3$	Prop. of Inequality for Exponential Functions
$2x > -2$	Add 1 to each side.
$x > -1$	Divide each side† by 2.

The solution set is $\{x \mid x > -1\}$.

Exercises

Solve each inequality.

1. $3^{x-4} < \frac{1}{27}$
$x < 1$

2. $4^{2x-2} > 2^{x+1}$
$x > \frac{5}{3}$

3. $5^{2x} < 125^{x-5}$
$x > 15$

4. $10^{4x+1} > 100^{x-2}$
$x > -\frac{5}{2}$

5. $7^{3x} < 49^{1-x}$
$x < \frac{2}{5}$

6. $8^{2x-5} < 4^{x+8}$
$x < \frac{31}{4}$

7. $16 \geq 4^{x+5}$
$x \leq -3$

8. $\left(\frac{1}{27}\right)^{2x+1} \leq \left(\frac{1}{243}\right)^{3x-2}$
$x \leq \frac{13}{9}$

9. $\left(\frac{1}{2}\right)^{x-3} > 8^{2x}$
$x < \frac{3}{7}$

10. $\frac{1}{81} < 9^{2x-4}$
$x > 1$

11. $32^{3x-4} > 128^{4x+3}$
$x > -\frac{41}{13}$

12. $27^{2x-5} < \left(\frac{1}{9}\right)^{5x}$
$x < \frac{15}{4}$

13. $\left(\frac{1}{25}\right)^{2x-1} \leq 125^{3x+1}$
$x \geq -\frac{1}{13}$

14. $\left(\frac{7}{343}\right)^{x-3} \geq \left(\frac{1}{49}\right)^{2x+1}$
$x \geq -4$

15. $\left(\frac{9}{27}\right)^{6x-1} \geq \left(\frac{27}{9}\right)^{-x+6}$
$x > -1$

NAME _____ DATE _____ PERIOD _____

8-2 Study Guide and Intervention

Solving Exponential Equations and Inequalities

Solve Exponential Equations All the properties of rational exponents that you know also apply to real exponents. Remember that $a^m \cdot a^n = a^{m+n}$, $(a^m)^n = a^{mn}$, and $a^m \div a^n = a^{m-n}$.

Property of Equality for Exponential Functions	If b is a positive number other than 1, then $b^x = b^y$ if and only if $x = y$.

Example 1 Solve $4^{x-1} = 2^{x+5}$.

$4^{x-1} = 2^{x+5}$	Original equation
$(2^2)^{x-1} = 2^{x+5}$	Rewrite 4 as 2^2.
$2(x-1) = x + 5$	Prop. of Inequality for Exponential Functions
$2x - 2 = x + 5$	Distributive Property
$x = 7$	Subtract x and add 2 to each side.

Example 2 Write an exponential function whose graph passes through the points (0, 3) and (4, 81).

The y-intercept is (0, 3), so $a = 3$. Since the other point is (4, 81), $b = \sqrt[4]{\frac{81}{3}}$.

Simplifying $\sqrt[4]{\frac{81}{3}} = \sqrt[4]{27} \approx 2.280$, the equation is $y = 3(2.280)^x$.

Exercises

Solve each equation.

1. $3^{2x-1} = 3^{x+2}$ **3**

2. $2^{3x} = 4^{x+2}$ **4**

3. $3^{3x-1} = \frac{1}{9}$ $-\frac{1}{2}$

4. $4^{x+1} = 8^{2x+3}$ $-\frac{7}{4}$

5. $8^{x-2} = \frac{1}{16}$ $\frac{2}{3}$

6. $25^{2x} = 125^{x+2}$ **6**

7. $9^{x+1} = 27^{x+4}$ **−10**

8. $36^{2x+4} = 216^{x+5}$ **7**

9. $\left(\frac{1}{64}\right)^{x-2} = 16^{3x+1}$ $\frac{4}{9}$

Write an exponential function for the graph that passes through the given points.

10. (0, 4) and (2, 36)
$y = 4(3)^x$

11. (0, 6) and (1, 81)
$y = 6(13.5)^x$

12. (0, 5) and (6, 320)
$y = 5(2)^x$

13. (0, 2) and (5, 486)
$y = 2(3)^x$

14. (0, 8) and $\left(3, \frac{27}{8}\right)$
$y = 8\left(\frac{3}{4}\right)^x$

15. (0, 1) and (4, 625)
$y = (5)^x$

16. (0, 3) and (3, 24)
$y = 3(2)^x$

17. (0, 12) and (4, 144)
$y = 12(1.861)^x$

18. (0, 9) and (2, 49)
$y = 9(2.333)^x$

Answers (Lesson 8-2)

NAME _____ DATE _____ PERIOD _____

8-2 Practice

Solving Exponential Equations and Inequalities

Solve each equation.

1. $4^{x+35} = 64^{4-3}$

$x = 22$

2. $\left(\frac{1}{64}\right)^{0.5x-3} = 8^{9x-2}$

$x = 0.8$

3. $3^{x-4} = 9^{x+28}$

$x = -60$

4. $\left(\frac{1}{4}\right)^{2x+2} = 64^{x-1}$

$x = \frac{1}{5}$

5. $\left(\frac{1}{2}\right)^{x-3} = 16^{3x+1}$

$x = -\frac{1}{13}$

6. $3^{6x-2} = \left(\frac{1}{9}\right)^{x+1}$

$x = 0$

Write an exponential function for the graph that passes through the given points.

7. (0, 5) and (4, 3125)

$y = 5(5)^x$

8. (0, 8) and (4, 2048)

$y = 8(4)^x$

9. $\left(0, \frac{3}{4}\right)$ and (2, 36.75)

$y = 0.75(7)^x$

10. (0, −0.2) and (−3, −3.125)

$y = -0.2(0.4)^x$

11. (0, 15) and $\left(2, \frac{15}{16}\right)$

$y = 15\left(\frac{1}{4}\right)^x$

12. (0, 0.7) and $\left(\frac{1}{2}, 3.5\right)$

$y = 0.7(25)^x$

Solve each inequality.

13. $400 > \left(\frac{1}{20}\right)^{7x+8}$

$x > -\frac{10}{7}$

14. $10^{2x+7} \geq 1000^x$

$x \leq 7$

15. $\left(\frac{1}{16}\right)^{3x-4} \leq 64^{x-1}$

$x \geq \frac{11}{9}$

16. $\left(\frac{1}{8}\right)^{x-6} < 4^{4x+5}$

$x > \frac{8}{11}$

17. $\left(\frac{1}{36}\right)^{1x+8} \leq 216^{x-3}$

$x \geq -\frac{7}{5}$

18. $128^{x+3} < \left(\frac{1}{1024}\right)^{2x}$

$x < \frac{7}{9}$

19. At time t, there are 216^{t+18} bacteria of type A and 36^{2t+8} bacteria of type B organisms in a sample. When will the number of each type of bacteria be equal?

$t = 38$

NAME _____ DATE _____ PERIOD _____

8-2 Skills Practice

Solving Exponential Equations and Inequalities

Solve each equation.

1. $25^{2x+3} = 25^{5x-9}$

4

2. $9^{9x-4} = 81^{3x+6}$

8

3. $4^{x-5} = 16^{2x-31}$

19

4. $4^{3x-3} = 8^{4x-4}$

1

5. $9^{x+5} = 27^{6x-10}$

2

6. $125^{3x-4} = 25^{4x+2}$

16

Solve each inequality.

7. $\left(\frac{1}{36}\right)^{6x-3} > 6^{3x-9}$

$x < 1$

8. $64^{4x-8} < 256^{2x+6}$

$x < 12$

9. $\left(\frac{1}{27}\right)^{3x+13} \leq 9^{3x-\frac{1}{2}}$

$x \geq -2$

10. $\left(\frac{1}{9}\right)^{2x+7} \leq 27^{6x-12}$

$x \leq 1$

11. $\left(\frac{1}{8}\right)^{-2x-6} > \left(\frac{1}{32}\right)^{-x+11}$

$x > -73$

12. $9^{9x+1} < \left(\frac{1}{243}\right)^{-3x+5}$

$x < -9$

Write an exponential function whose graph passes through the given points.

13. (0, 3) and (3, 375)

$y = 3(5)^x$

14. (0, −1) and (6, −64)

$y = -1(2)^x$

15. (0, 7) and (−2, 28)

$y = 7\left(\frac{1}{2}\right)^x$

16. $\left(0, \frac{1}{2}\right)$ and (2, 40.5)

$y = \frac{1}{2}(9)^x$

17. (0, 15) and (1, 12)

$y = 15(0.8)^x$

18. (0, −6) and (−4, −1536)

$y = -6\left(\frac{1}{4}\right)^x$

19. $\left(0, \frac{1}{3}\right)$ and (3, 9)

$y = \frac{1}{3}(3)^x$

20. (0, 1) and (6, 4096)

$y = (4)^x$

21. (0, −2) and (−1, −4)

$y = -2\left(\frac{1}{2}\right)^x$

Lesson 8-2

NAME _____ DATE _____ PERIOD _____

8-2 Enrichment

Richter Scale

In 1935, Charles Richter and Beno Gutenberg working in California recognized that seismic waves that are radiated by earthquakes could be a way to estimate the magnitude or strength of an earthquake. Using a piece of equipment known as a Wood-Anderson seismograph, they developed the Richter scale. They discovered that the magnitude of an earthquake is equal to the base-10 logarithm of the amplitude of the wave recorded by the seismograph plus a correction factor based on the location of the seismograph or $M = \log_{10} A + CF$. With the magnitude, the amount of seismic energy in erg of the earthquake can be calculated using the formula $E_s = 10^{11.8 + 1.5M}$.

1. The largest earthquake ever recorded was in Chile in 1960. It released about 1.995×10^{25} erg.

   a. On the Richter scale what was the magnitude of this earthquake? Round to the nearest tenth. **9**

   b. Assume that the seismograph that records this has a correction factor of 6.2, what would be the amplitude of wave recorded by the seismograph? Round to the nearest hundredth. **630.95**

2. The amount of seismic energy released divided by 6.4×10^8 would give the number of ounces of TNT (dynamite) needed for a comparable destructive force.

   a. The largest thermonuclear weapon created has a destructive force of 32 million tons of dynamite. How many ergs is this? **about 1.995×10^{22} erg**

   b. What would be the magnitude of this force on the Richter scale? **7**

3. Using dynamite in a lab a rock is broken and the results are recorded with a seismograph. Assuming a correction factor of .3, there was an amplitude of about 0.0158.

   a. What would be the magnitude of this on the Richter scale? **−1.5**

   b. How much seismic energy would be released by this action? Express your answer in scientific notation. **about 3.548×10^9 erg**

   c. How many ounces of dynamite were used? **about 5.5 oz**

Chapter 8   17   Glencoe Algebra 2

NAME _____ DATE _____ PERIOD _____

8-2 Word Problem Practice

Solving Exponential Equations and Inequalities

1. **BANKING** The certificate of deposit that Siobhan bought on her birthday pays interest according to the formula $A = 1200\left(1 + \frac{0.052}{12}\right)^{48}$. What is the annual interest rate? **5.2%**

2. **INTEREST** Marty invested $2000 in an account that pays at least 4% annual interest. He wants to see how much money he will have over the next few years. Graph the inequality $y \geq 2000(1 + 0.04)^x$ to show his potential earnings.

3. **BUSINESS** Ahmed's consulting firm began with 23 clients. After 7 years, he now has 393 clients. Write an exponential equation describing the firm's growth. **$y = 23(1.5)^x$**

4. **POPULATION** In 2000, the world population was calculated to be 6,071,675,206. In 2008, it was 6,679,493,893. Write an exponential equation to model the growth of the world population over these 8 years. Round the base to the nearest thousandth.

   Source: U.S. Census Bureau

   $y = 6,071,675,206(1.012)^x$

5. **BUSINESS** Ingrid and Alberto each opened a business in 2000. Ingrid started with 2 employees and in 2003 she had 50 employees. Alberto began with 32 employees and in 2007 he had 310 employees. Since 2000, each company has experienced exponential growth.

   a. Write an exponential equation representing the growth for each business.

   Ingrid: $y = 2(2.924)^x$;
   Alberto: $y = 32(1.383)^x$

   b. Calculate the number of employees each company had in 2005.

   Ingrid: 427; Alberto: 162

   c. Is it reasonable to expect that a business can experience exponential growth? Explain your answer.

   Sample answer: No; a business cannot grow exponentially indefinitely.

Chapter 8   16   Glencoe Algebra 2

8-2 Graphing Calculator Activity

Solving Exponential Equations and Inequalities

Exponential equations and inequalities can be solved on a graphing calculator or on a TI-Nspire.

Example Solve $5^{(2x+5)} = 125^{(x+2.5)} - 2$.

Step 1: Enter $5^{(2x+5)}$ as **Y1** and $125^{(x+2.5)} - 2$ as **Y2**.

Keystrokes: [Y=] 5 [^] (2 [X,T,θ,n] + 5) [ENTER]
125 [^] ([X,T,θ,n] + 2 . 5) − 2 [ENTER]

Then graph the two equations.

Keystrokes: [GRAPH]

Step 2: Use the Intersect function on the CALC menu to estimate the solution.

Keystrokes: [2nd] [CALC] 5 [ENTER] [ENTER] [ENTER]

The intersection is at approximately (−2.17, 2.88).

Check your solution: Substituting −2.17 for x, $5^{(0.66)} \approx 125^{(0.33)} - 2$.

Exercises

Solve each exponential equation or inequality with a graphing calculator.

1. $3^{4x+7} = 27^{4x-3}$

   x = 2

2. $16^{(2x+5)} > 64^{3x-2}$

   x < 3.2

3. $343^{3x-9} = 49^{x+6}$

   x = 9.75

4. $128^{-5} < 16^{2x-5}$

   x > −15

5. $625^{2x-1} = 25^{3x+4}$

   x = 2

6. $3^{x+1} = 6^{x-2}$

   x ≈ 6.75

7. $16^{2x-1} - 4 = 8^{-x+2}$

   x ≈ 0.959

8. $3^{3x} = 4^{x-1}$

   −1.710

8-3 Study Guide and Intervention

Logarithms and Logarithmic Functions

Logarithmic Functions and Expressions

Definition of Logarithm with Base b	Let b and x be positive numbers, $b \neq 1$. The logarithm of x with base b is denoted $\log_b x$ and is defined as the exponent y that makes the equation $b^y = x$ true.

The inverse of the exponential function $y = b^x$ is the **logarithmic function** $x = b^y$. This function is usually written as $y = \log_b x$.

Example 1 Write an exponential equation equivalent to $\log_3 243 = 5$.

$3^5 = 243$

Example 2 Write a logarithmic equation equivalent to $6^{-3} = \frac{1}{216}$.

$\log_6 \frac{1}{216} = -3$

Example 3 Evaluate $\log_8 16$.

$8^{\frac{4}{3}} = 16$, so $\log_8 16 = \frac{4}{3}$.

Exercises

Write each equation in exponential form.

1. $\log_{15} 225 = 2$
   $15^2 = 225$

2. $\log_3 \frac{1}{27} = -3$
   $3^{-3} = \frac{1}{27}$

3. $\log_4 32 = \frac{5}{2}$
   $4^{\frac{5}{2}} = 32$

Write each equation in logarithmic form.

4. $2^7 = 128$
   $\log_2 128 = 7$

5. $3^{-4} = \frac{1}{81}$
   $\log_3 \frac{1}{81} = -4$

6. $\left(\frac{1}{7}\right)^3 = \frac{1}{343}$
   $\log_{\frac{1}{7}} \frac{1}{343} = 3$

7. $7^{-2} = \frac{1}{49}$
   $\log_7 \frac{1}{49} = -2$

8. $2^9 = 512$
   $\log_2 512 = 9$

9. $64^{\frac{2}{3}} = 16$
   $\log_{64} 16 = \frac{2}{3}$

Evaluate each expression.

10. $\log_4 64$
    3

11. $\log_2 64$
    6

12. $\log_{100} 100{,}000$
    2.5

13. $\log_5 625$
    4

14. $\log_{27} 81$
    $\frac{4}{3}$

15. $\log_{25} 5$
    $\frac{1}{2}$

16. $\log_2 \frac{1}{128}$
    −7

17. $\log_{10} 0.00001$
    −5

18. $\log_4 \frac{1}{32}$
    −2.5

Lesson 8-3

NAME _____ DATE _____ PERIOD _____

8-3 Skills Practice

Logarithms and Logarithmic Functions

Write each equation in exponential form.

1. $\log_3 243 = 5$ $3^5 = 243$

2. $\log_4 64 = 3$ $4^3 = 64$

3. $\log_9 3 = \frac{1}{2}$ $9^{\frac{1}{2}} = 3$

4. $\log_5 \frac{1}{25} = -2$ $5^{-2} = \frac{1}{25}$

Write each equation in logarithmic form.

5. $2^3 = 8$ $\log_2 8 = 3$

6. $3^2 = 9$ $\log_3 9 = 2$

7. $8^{-2} = \frac{1}{64}$ $\log_8 \frac{1}{64} = -2$

8. $\left(\frac{1}{3}\right)^2 = \frac{1}{9}$ $\log_{\frac{1}{3}} \frac{1}{9} = 2$

Evaluate each expression.

9. $\log_5 25$ **2**

10. $\log_9 3$ $\frac{1}{2}$

11. $\log_{10} 1000$ **3**

12. $\log_{125} 5$ $\frac{1}{3}$

13. $\log_4 64$ **3**

14. $\log_5 \frac{1}{625}$ **−4**

15. $\log_8 512$ **3**

16. $\log_{27} \frac{1}{3}$ $-\frac{1}{3}$

Graph each function.

17. $f(x) = \log_5(x + 1) - 4$

18. $f(x) = -\log_5 x + 2.5$

Chapter 8   21   *Glencoe Algebra 2*

NAME _____ DATE _____ PERIOD _____

8-3 Study Guide and Intervention *(continued)*

Logarithms of Logarithmic Functions

Graphing Logarithmic Functions The function $y = \log_b x$, where $b \neq 1$, is called a logarithmic function. The graph of $f(x) = \log_b x$ represents a parent graph of the logarithmic functions. Properties of the parent function are described in the following table.

Parent function of Logarithmic Functions, $f(x) = \log_b x$	1. The function is continuous and one-to-one. 2. The domain is the set of all positive real numbers. 3. The y-axis is an asymptote of the graph. 4. The range is the set of all real numbers. 5. The graph contains the point (1, 0).

The graphs of logarithmic functions can be transformed by changing the value of the constants a, h, and k in the equation $f(x) = a \log_b (x - h) + k$.

Example   Graph $f(x) = -3 \log_{10}(x - 2) + 1$.

This is a transformation of the graph of $f(x) = \log_{10} x$.

• $|a| = 3$: The graph expands vertically.
• $a < 0$: The graph is reflected across the x-axis.
• $h = 2$: The graph is translated 2 units to the right.
• $k = 1$: The graph is translated 1 unit up.

Exercises

Graph each function.

1. $f(x) = 4 \log_2 x$

2. $f(x) = 4 \log_3 (x - 1)$

3. $f(x) = 2 \log_4 (x + 3) - 2$

Chapter 8   20   *Glencoe Algebra 2*

Answers (Lesson 8-3)

NAME _____ DATE _____ PERIOD _____

8-3 Word Problem Practice

Logarithms and Logarithmic Functions

1. **CHEMISTRY** The pH of a solution is found by the formula pH = −log H, where H stands for the hydrogen ion concentration in the formula. What is the pH of a solution to the nearest hundredth when H is 1356?

−3.13

2. **FIND THE ERROR** Michio wanted to find the value of x in the equation $2(3)^x = 34$. He first converted the equation to $\log_3 2x = 17$. Next he wrote $2x = 3^{17}$ and used a calculator to find $x = 64{,}570{,}081$. Was his answer correct? If not, what was his mistake and what is the right answer?

No; he should have converted to $x = \log_3 17$; $x = 2.58$.

3. **SOUND** The decibel level L of a sound is determined by the formula $L = 10 \log_{10} \frac{I}{M}$. Find I in terms of M for a noise with a decibel level of 120.

$I = 1{,}000{,}000{,}000{,}000\ M$ or $10^{12}\ M$

4. **EARTHQUAKES** The intensity of an earthquake can be measured on the Richter scale using the formula $y = 10^{R-1}$, where y is the absolute intensity of the earthquake and R is its Richter scale measurement.

Richter Scale Number	Absolute Intensity
1	1
2	10
3	100
4	1000
5	10,000

An earthquake in San Francisco in 1906 had an absolute intensity of 6,000,000. What was that earthquake's measurement on the Richter scale?

7.8

5. **GAMES** Julio and Natalia decided to play a game in which they each selected a logarithmic function and compare their functions to see which gave larger values. Julio selected the function $f(x) = 10 \log_4 x$ and Natalia selected the function $2 \log_{10} x$.

a. Which of the functions has a larger value when $x = 7$?
Julio's; Julio's is 28.07 and Natalia's is 1.69.

b. Which of their functions has a larger value when $x = 1$?
Neither; both equal 0.

c. Do you think the base or the multiplier is more important in determining the value of a logarithmic function?
Answers will vary.

Chapter 8   23   Glencoe Algebra 2

NAME _____ DATE _____ PERIOD _____

8-3 Practice

Logarithms and Logarithmic Functions

Write each equation in exponential form.

1. $\log_6 216 = 3$ **$6^3 = 216$**
2. $\log_2 64 = 6$ **$2^6 = 64$**
3. $\log_3 \frac{1}{81} = -4$ **$3^{-4} = \frac{1}{81}$**
4. $\log_{10} 0.00001 = -5$ **$10^{-5} = 0.00001$**
5. $\log_{25} 5 = \frac{1}{2}$ **$25^{\frac{1}{2}} = 5$**
6. $\log_{32} 8 = \frac{3}{5}$ **$35^{\frac{3}{5}} = 8$**

Write each equation in logarithmic form.

7. $5^3 = 125$ **$\log_5 125 = 3$**
8. $7^0 = 1$ **$\log_7 1 = 0$**
9. $3^4 = 81$ **$\log_3 81 = 4$**
10. $3^{-4} = \frac{1}{81}$ **$\log_3 \frac{1}{81} = -4$**
11. $\left(\frac{1}{4}\right)^3 = \frac{1}{64}$ **$\log_{\frac{1}{4}} \frac{1}{64} = 3$**
12. $7776^{\frac{1}{5}} = 6$ **$\log_{7776} 6 = \frac{1}{5}$**

Evaluate each expression.

13. $\log_3 81$ **4**
14. $\log_{10} 0.0001$ **−4**
15. $\log_2 \frac{1}{16}$ **−4**
16. $\log_{\frac{1}{3}} 27$ **−3**
17. $\log_9 1$ **0**
18. $\log_8 4$ **$\frac{2}{3}$**
19. $\log_7 \frac{1}{49}$ **−2**
20. $\log_6 6^4$ **4**

Graph each function.

21. $f(x) = \log_2 (x - 2)$

22. $f(x) = -2 \log_4 x$

23. **SOUND** An equation for loudness, in decibels, is $L = 10 \log_{10} R$, where R is the relative intensity of the sound. Sounds that reach levels of 120 decibels or more are painful to humans. What is the relative intensity of 120 decibels? **10^{12}**

24. **INVESTING** Maria invests $1000 in a savings account that pays 4% interest compounded annually. The value of the account A at the end of five years can be determined from the equation $\log_{10} A = \log_{10} [1000(1 + 0.04)^5]$. Write this equation in exponential form.

$A = 1000(1 + 0.04)^5$

Chapter 8   22   Glencoe Algebra 2

Answers (Lesson 8-3)

NAME _____ DATE _____ PERIOD _____

8-3 TI-Nspire Calculator Activity

Logarithms and Logarithmic Functions

Logarithmic functions can be graphed on a graphing calculator or on a TI-Nspire.

Example 1 Graph $y = \log_5 (2x - 3)$.

Use the Graphs and Geometry function from the home menu to enter the equation.

Keystrokes: (menu) 2 (enter) (ctrl) 5 ▶ 2 (X) (−) 3 (enter)

Example 2 Find the intersection of $\log_5 (2x - 3)$ and $\log_8 (4x + 6)$ by graphing.

On the screen of $\log_5 (2x - 3)$, enter $\log_8 (4x + 6)$ on the $f2(x)$ line.

Keystrokes: (ctrl) (enter) 8 ▶ 4 (X) (−) 6 (enter)

Now, use the intersection function to find the coordinates of the intersection.

Keystrokes: (ctrl) 63

Use the arrow keys to move the pointer ↖ to the graph of $f1(x)$ and click, then move the pointer to the graph of $f2(x)$ and click. Use the arrow keys to move the pointer to the label of the intersection, and hold down the (?) button until the open hand on the screen closes (✋). You can then use the arrow keys to move the label of the intersection until the full coordinates are visible on the TI-Nspire screen.

The intersection point for $\log_5 (2x - 3)$ and $\log_8 (4x + 6)$ is approximately (13.22, 1.96).

Exercises

Graph these logarithmic equations on a TI-Nspire.

1. $y = -3 \log_{18} (x - 9) + 2$
2. $y = 4 \log_{11} (2 - x) + 3$
3. $y = 4 \log_2 (x - 2) + 2$

4. Find the intersection of $2 \log_7 (x - 3)$ and $\log_4 (2x - 1) - 1$. **(4.68, 0.53)**

Chapter 8   25   Glencoe Algebra 2

NAME _____ DATE _____ PERIOD _____

8-3 Enrichment

Comparing Logarithmic Graphs

Solve the problems below to relate the graphs of $y = \log_n ax$.

1. Graph the functions $y = \log_2 x$,
$y = \log_3 x$, $y = \log_4 x$.

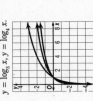

What can you conclude about the graph of $y = \log_n ax$ as the value of n increases and a is constant?
As the value of n increases the dilation of the graph changes.

2. Graph the functions $y = \log_2 x$,
$y = \log_2 2x$, $y = \log_2 4x$.

What can you conclude about the graph of $y = \log_n ax$ as the value of a increases and n is constant?
The intersection along the x-axis moves to the left and the intersection along the y-axis moves up.

3. Graph the functions $y = \log_2 (-2x)$,
$y = \log_2 (-x)$, $y = \log_2 x$, $y = \log_2 2x$.

What can you conclude about the graph of $y = \log_n ax$ for a and $-a$ as n stays constant?
The graph of $y = \log_n -ax$ is a mirror image of $y = \log_n ax$ over the y-axis.

4. Graph the functions $y = \log_{\frac{1}{4}} x$, $y = \log_{\frac{1}{2}}$
x, $y = \log_2 x$, $y = \log_4 x$.

What can you conclude about the graph of $y = \log_n ax$ for n and $\frac{1}{n}$ as s stays constant?
The graph of $y = \log_{\frac{1}{n}} x$ is a mirror image of $y = \log_n ax$ over the x-axis.

5. Without graphing, describe the graph of $y = \log_{\frac{1}{4}} (-4x)$ using the conclusions you found in Exercises 1–4.
The graph of $y = \log_{\frac{1}{4}} (-4x)$ is dilated so it is closer to the x-axis than $y = \log_{\frac{1}{2}} (-4x)$ it is reflected over the x and y-axis, it is translated along the x-axis to the right of $y = \log_2 x$, and it is translated along the x-axis to the down of $y = \log_{\frac{1}{4}} (-4x)$

Chapter 8   24   Glencoe Algebra 2

Answers (Lesson 8-4)

NAME _____ DATE _____ PERIOD _____

8-4 Study Guide and Intervention
Solving Logarithmic Equations and Inequalities

Solving Logarithmic Equations

Property of Equality for Logarithmic Functions	If b is a positive number other than 1, then $\log_b x = \log_b y$ if and only if $x = y$.

Example 1 Solve $\log_2 2x = 3$.

$\log_2 2x = 3$ Original equation
$2x = 2^3$ Definition of logarithm
$2x = 8$ Simplify.
$x = 4$ Simplify.

The solution is $x = 4$.

Example 2 Solve the equation $\log_2 (x + 17) = \log_2 (3 + 23)$.

Since the bases of the logarithms are equal, $(x + 17)$ must equal $(3x + 23)$.

$(x + 17) = (3x + 23)$
$-6 = 2x$
$x = -3$.

Exercises

Solve each equation.

1. $\log_2 32 = 3x$ $\frac{5}{3}$
2. $\log_3 2x = -2$ $\frac{1}{18}$
3. $\log_4 16 = -2$ $\frac{1}{8}$
4. $\log_{25} \left(\frac{x}{2}\right) = \frac{1}{2}$ 10
5. $\log_4 (5x + 1) = 2$ 3
6. $\log_8 (x - 5) = \frac{2}{3}$ 9
7. $\log_4 (3x - 1) = \log_4 (2x + 3)$ 4
8. $\log_2 (x^2 - 6) = \log_2 (2x + 2)$ 4
9. $\log_{x+4} 27 = 3$ −1
10. $\log_2 (x + 3) = 4$ 13
11. $\log_x 1000 = 3$ 10
12. $\log_8 (4x + 4) = 2$ 15
13. $\log_2 x = \log_2 12$ x = 12
14. $\log_3 (x - 5) = \log_3 13$ x = 18
15. $\log_{10} x = \log_{10} (5x - 20)$ x = 5
16. $\log_5 x = \log_5 (2x - 1)$ x = 1
17. $\log_4 (x + 12) = \log_4 4x$ x = 4
18. $\log_6 (x - 3) = \log_6 2x$ no solution

Chapter 8   26   Glencoe Algebra 2

NAME _____ DATE _____ PERIOD _____

8-4 Study Guide and Intervention (continued)
Solving Logarithmic Equations and Inequalities

Solving Logarithmic Inequalities

Property of Inequality for Logarithmic Functions	If $b > 1$, $x > 0$, and $\log_b x > y$, then $x > b^y$. If $b > 1$, $x > 0$, and $\log_b x < y$, then $0 < x < b^y$. If $b > 1$, then $\log_b x > \log_b y$ if and only if $x > y$, and $\log_b x < \log_b y$ if and only if $x < y$.

Example 1 Solve $\log_5 (4x - 3) < 3$.

$\log_5 (4x - 3) < 3$ Original equation
$0 < 4x - 3 < 5^3$ Property of Inequality
$3 < 4x < 125 + 3$ Simplify.
$\frac{3}{4} < x < 32$ Simplify.

The solution set is $\left\{x \mid \frac{3}{4} < x < 32\right\}$.

Example 2 Solve the inequality $\log_8 (3x - 4) < \log_8 (x + 1)$.

$\log_8 (3x - 4) < \log_8 (x + 1)$.
Since the base of the logarithms are equal to or greater than 1, $3x - 4 < x + 1$.
$2x < 5$
$x < \frac{5}{2}$

Since $3x - 4$ and $x + 1$ must both be positive numbers, solve $3x - 4 = 0$ for the lower bound of the inequality.
The solution is $\left\{x \mid \frac{4}{3} < x < \frac{5}{2}\right\}$.

Exercises

Solve each inequality.

1. $\log_2 2x > 2$ $\{x \mid x > 2\}$
2. $\log_5 x > 2$ $\{x \mid x > 25\}$
3. $\log_2 (3x + 1) < 4$ $\left\{x \mid -\frac{1}{3} < x < 5\right\}$
4. $\log_4 2x > -\frac{1}{2}$ $\left\{x \mid x > \frac{1}{4}\right\}$
5. $\log_3 (x + 3) < 3$ $\{x \mid -3 < x < 24\}$
6. $\log_{27} 6x > \frac{2}{3}$ $\left\{x \mid x > \frac{3}{2}\right\}$
7. $\log_{10} 5x < \log_{10} 30$ $\{x \mid 0 < x < 6\}$
8. $\log_{10} x < \log_{10} (2x - 4)$ $\{x \mid x > 4\}$
9. $\log_{10} 3x < \log_{10} (7x - 8)$ $\{x \mid x > 2\}$
10. $\log_2 (8x + 5) > \log_2 (9x - 18)$ $\{x \mid 2 < x < 23\}$
11. $\log_{10} (3x + 7) < \log_{10} (7x - 3)$ $\left\{x \mid x > 2\frac{1}{2}\right\}$
12. $\log_2 (3x - 4) < \log_2 2x + 7$ $\left\{x \mid 1\frac{1}{3} < x < 11\right\}$

Chapter 8   27   Glencoe Algebra 2

Answers (Lesson 8-4)

NAME _____ DATE _____ PERIOD _____

8-4 Practice

Solving Logarithmic Equations and Inequalities

Solve each equation.

1. $x + 5 = \log_4 256$ $x = -1$

2. $3x - 5 = \log_2 1024$ $x = 5$

3. $\log_3 (4x - 17) = 5$ $x = 65$

4. $\log_5 (3 - x) = 5$ $x = -3122$

5. $\log_{13} (x^2 - 4) = \log_{13} 3x$ $x = 4$

6. $\log_6 (x - 5) = \log_3 (3x - 25)$ $x = 10$

Solve each inequality

7. $\log_8 (-6x) < 1$ $\{x \mid 0 > x > -\frac{4}{3}\}$

8. $\log_9 (x + 2) > \log_9 (6 - 3x)$ $\{x \mid -2 > x > 1\}$

9. $\log_{11} (x + 7) < 1$ $\{x \mid -7 < x < 4\}$

10. $\log_{81} x \le 0.75$ $\{x \mid 27 \ge x > 0\}$

11. $\log_2 (x + 6) < \log_2 17$ $\{x \mid 11 > x > -6\}$

12. $\log_{12} (2x - 1) > \log_{12} (5x - 16)$ $\{x \mid 3\frac{1}{5} < x < 5\}$

13. $\log_9 (2x - 1) < 0.5$ $\{x \mid 0.5 < x < 2\}$

14. $\log_{10} (x - 5) > \log_{10} 2x$ no solution

15. $\log_3 (x + 12) > \log_3 2x$ $\{x \mid 12 > x > 0\}$

16. $\log_3 (0.3x + 5) > \log_3 (x - 2)$ $\{x \mid 2 < x < 10\}$

17. $\log_2 (x + 3) < \log_2 (1 - 3x)$ no solution

18. $\log_6 (3 - x) \le \log_6 (x - 1)$ $\{x \mid 3 > x \ge 2\}$

19. **WILDLIFE** An ecologist discovered that the population of a certain endangered species has been doubling every 12 years. When the population reaches 20 times the current level, it may no longer be endangered. Write the logarithmic expression that gives the number of years it will take for the population to reach that level.
$12 \log_2 20$

NAME _____ DATE _____ PERIOD _____

8-4 Skills Practice

Solving Logarithmic Equations and Inequalities

Solve each equation.

1. $3x = \log_6 216$ 1

2. $x - 4 = \log_3 243$ 9

3. $\log_4 (4x - 20) = 5$ 261

4. $\log_9 (3 - x) = \log_9 (5x - 15)$ 3

5. $\log_{81} (x + 20) = \log_{81} (6x)$ 4

6. $\log_9 (3x^2) = \log_9 (2x + 1)$ 1

7. $\log_4 (x - 1) = \log_4 (12)$ 13

8. $\log_7 (5 - x) = \log_7 (5)$ 0

9. $\log_2 (5x) = 2$ 5

Solve each inequality.

10. $\log_5 (-3x) < 1$ $\{x \mid -\frac{5}{3} < x < 0\}$

11. $\log_6 x > \log_6 (4 - x)$ $\{x \mid 2 < x < 4\}$

12. $\log_{10} (x - 3) > 2$ $\{x \mid 3 < x < 103\}$

13. $\log_2 (x - 5) > \log_2 (3)$ $\{x \mid x > 8\}$

14. $\log_7 (8x + 5) > \log_7 (6x - 18)$ $\{x \mid x > 3\}$

15. $\log_9 (3x - 3) < 1.5$ $\{x \mid 1 < x < 10\}$

16. $\log_{10} (2x - 2) < \log_{10} (7 - x)$ $\{x \mid 1 < x < 3\}$

17. $\log_9 (x - 1) > \log_9 (2x)$ no solution

18. $\log_{16} x \ge 0.5$ $\{x \mid x \ge 4\}$

19. $\log_3 \left(\frac{x - 3}{4} + 5\right) > \log_3 (x + 2)$ $\{x \mid -2 < x < 3\}$

20. $\log_5 (3x) < \log_5 (2x - 1)$ no solution

21. $\log_5 (7 - x) \le \log_5 (x + 19)$ $\{x \mid -6 \le x \le 7\}$

Answers (Lesson 8-4)

8-4 Word Problem Practice

Solving Logarithmic Equations and Inequalities

1. **FISH** The population of silver carp has been growing in the Mississippi River. About every 3 years, the population doubles. Write logarithmic expression that gives the number of years it will take for the population to increase by a factor of ten.

   $3 \log_2 10$

2. **POWERS** Haley tries to solve the equation $\log_4 2x = 5$. She got the wrong answer. What was her mistake? What should the correct answer be?

1.	$\log_4 2x = 5$
2.	$2x = 4^5$
3.	$x = 2^5$
4.	$x = 32$

   From step 2 to step 3, Haley divided the equation by 2 incorrectly. The correct answer is 512.

3. **DIGITS** A computer programmer wants to write a formula that tells how many digits there are in a number n, where n is a positive integer. For example, if $n = 343$, the formula should evaluate to 3 and if $n = 10,000$, the formula should evaluate to 5. Suppose $8 \le \log_{10} n < 9$. How many digits does n have?

   9

4. **LOGARITHMS** Pauline knows that $\log_b x = 3$ and $\log_b y = 5$. She knows that this is the same as knowing that $b^3 = x$ and $b^5 = y$. Multiply these two equations together and rewrite it as an equation involving logarithms. What is $\log_b xy$?

   $b^3 b^5 = xy$, or $b^8 = xy$; in other words, $\log_b xy = 8$

5. **MUSIC** The first note on a piano keyboard corresponds to a pitch with a frequency of 27.5 cycles per second.

   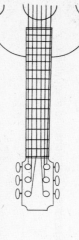

   With every successive note you go up the white and black keys of a piano, the pitch multiplies by a factor of $\sqrt[12]{2}$. The formula for the frequency of the pitch sounded when the nth note up the keyboard is played is given by

   $$n = 1 + 12 \log_2 \frac{f}{27.5}$$

   a. The pitch that orchestras tune to is the A above middle C. It has a frequency of 440 cycles per second. How many notes up the piano keyboard is this A?
   49

   b. Another pitch on the keyboard has a frequency of 1760 cycles per second. How many notes up the keyboard will this be found?
   73

Lesson 8-4

8-4 Enrichment

Musical Relationships

The frequencies of notes that are one octave apart in a musical scale are related by an exponential equation. For the eight C notes on a piano, the equation is $C_n = C_1 2^{n-1}$, where C_n represents the frequency of note C_n.

1. Find the relationship between C_1 and C_2. $\quad C_2 = 2C_1$

2. Find the relationship between C_1 and C_4. $\quad C_4 = 8C_1$

The frequencies of consecutive notes are related by a common ratio r. The general equation is $f_n = f_1 r^{n-1}$.

3. If the frequency of middle C is 261.6 cycles per second and the frequency of the next higher C is 523.2 cycles per second, find the common ratio r. (*Hint:* The two C's are 12 notes apart.) Write the answer as a radical expression.
   $r = \sqrt[12]{2}$

4. Substitute decimal values for r and f_1 to find a specific equation for f_n.
   $f_n = 261.1(1.05946)^{n-1}$

5. Find the frequency of F# above middle C.
   $f_7 = 261.6(1.05946)^6 \approx 369.95$

6. Frets are a series of ridges placed across the fingerboard of a guitar. They are spaced so that the sound made by pressing a string against one fret has about 1.0595 times the wavelength of the sound made by using the next fret. The general equation is $w_n = w_0(1.0595)^n$. Describe the arrangement of the frets on a guitar.

   The frets are spaced in a logarithmic scale.

Answers (Lesson 8-4 and Lesson 8-5)

Lesson 8-5

NAME _____ DATE _____ PERIOD _____

8-5 Study Guide and Intervention

Properties of Logarithms

Properties of Logarithms Properties of exponents can be used to develop the following properties of logarithms.

Product Property of Logarithms	For all positive numbers a, b, and x, where $x \neq 1$, $\log_x ab = \log_x a + \log_x b$.
Quotient Property of Logarithms	For all positive numbers a, b, and x, where $x \neq 1$, $\log_x \frac{a}{b} = \log_x a - \log_x b$.
Power Property of Logarithms	For any real number p and positive numbers m and b, where $b \neq 1$, $\log_b m^p = p \log_b m$.

Example Use $\log_3 28 \approx 3.0331$ and $\log_3 4 \approx 1.2619$ to approximate the value of each expression.

a. $\log_3 36$

$\log_3 36 = \log_3 (3^2 \cdot 4)$
$= \log_3 3^2 + \log_3 4$
$= 2 + \log_3 4$
$\approx 2 + 1.2619$
≈ 3.2619

b. $\log_3 7$

$\log_3 7 = \log_3 \left(\frac{28}{4}\right)$
$= \log_3 28 - \log_3 4$
$\approx 3.0331 - 1.2619$
≈ 1.7712

c. $\log_3 256$

$\log_3 256 = \log_3 (4^4)$
$= 4 \cdot \log_3 4$
$\approx 4(1.2619)$
≈ 5.0476

Exercises

Use $\log_{12} 3 \approx 0.4421$ and $\log_{12} 7 \approx 0.7831$ to approximate the value of each expression.

1. $\log_{12} 21$ **1.2252**

2. $\log_{12} \frac{7}{3}$ **0.3410**

3. $\log_{12} 49$ **1.5662**

4. $\log_{12} 36$ **1.4421**

5. $\log_{12} 63$ **1.6673**

6. $\log_{12} \frac{27}{49}$ **−0.2399**

7. $\log_{12} \frac{81}{49}$ **0.2022**

8. $\log_{12} 16,807$ **3.9155**

9. $\log_{12} 441$ **2.4504**

Use $\log_5 3 \approx 0.6826$ and $\log_5 4 \approx 0.8614$ to approximate the value of each expression.

10. $\log_5 12$ **1.5440**

11. $\log_5 100$ **2.8614**

12. $\log_5 0.75$ **−0.1788**

13. $\log_5 144$ **3.0880**

14. $\log_5 \frac{27}{16}$ **0.3250**

15. $\log_5 375$ **3.6826**

16. $\log_5 1.\overline{3}$ **0.1788**

17. $\log_5 \frac{9}{16}$ **−0.3576**

18. $\log_5 \frac{81}{5}$ **1.7304**

Lesson 8-4

NAME _____ DATE _____ PERIOD _____

8-4 TI-Nspire Calculator Activity

Evaluating Logarithmic Equations and Inequalities

Logarithmic equations and inequalities can be evaluated on a graphing calculator or on a TI-Nspire.

Example 1 Graph $y = \log_{10}(5x - 1)$ on a graphing calculator.

Keystrokes: (on) 2 (ctrl) (ex) 10 ▸ 5 (X) 1 (enter)

Example 2 Find the intersection of $\log_{10}(5x - 1)$ and $\log_{10}(3x + 2)$ using the table function.

On the screen of $\log_{10}(5x - 1)$, enter $\log_{10}(3x + 2)$ on the $f2(x)$ line.

Keystrokes: (enter) (ctrl) (ex) 10 ▸ 3 (X) 2 (enter)·

Now, use the table function to find the coordinates of the intersection.

Keystrokes: (menu) 28 (enter) 53 ▾ 0 (·) 1 (enter)·

Click the (X) button to move past the error message alerting you that there are values for which the logarithmic functions are undefined. Then use the arrow keys to move down the table to find the value where $f1(x)$ equals $f2(x)$. The functions intersect at approximately the point (1.5, 0.81).

Exercises

Estimate the solutions for these logarithmic equations by finding the intersections of the graphs on a TI-Nspire.

1. $\log_{10}(8x + 7)$ and $\log_{10}(15x - 21)$ **4**

2. $\log_{10}(x + 1)$ and $\log_{10}(2x - 8)$ **9**

3. $\log_{10}(5x + 2)$ and $\log_{10}(10x - 3)$ **1**

4. $\log_{10}(3x + 2)$ and $\log_{10}(4x - 3)$ **5**

5. $\log_{10}(14x - 5)$ and $\log_{10}(10x - 3)$ **0.5**

6. $\log_{10}(7x - 6)$ and $\log_{10}(3x + 1)$ **1.7**

NAME ___ DATE ___ PERIOD ___

8-5 Study Guide and Intervention (continued)

Properties of Logarithms

Solve Logarithmic Equations You can use the properties of logarithms to solve equations involving logarithms.

Example Solve each equation.

a. $2 \log_3 x - \log_3 4 = \log_3 25$

$2 \log_3 x - \log_3 4 = \log_3 25$ Original equation
$\log_3 x^2 - \log_3 4 = \log_3 25$ Power Property
$\log_3 \dfrac{x^2}{4} = \log_3 25$ Quotient Property
$\dfrac{x^2}{4} = 25$ Property of Equality for Logarithmic Functions
$x^2 = 100$ Multiply each side by 4.
$x = \pm 10$ Take the square root of each side.

Since logarithms are undefined for $x < 0$, -10 is an extraneous solution. The only solution is 10.

b. $\log_2 x + \log_2 (x + 2) = 3$

$\log_2 x + \log_2 (x + 2) = 3$ Original equation
$\log_2 x(x + 2) = 3$ Product Property
$x(x + 2) = 2^3$ Definition of logarithm
$x^2 + 2x = 8$ Distributive Property
$x^2 + 2x - 8 = 0$ Subtract 8 from each side.
$(x + 4)(x - 2) = 0$ Factor.
$x = 2$ or $x = -4$ Zero Product Property

Since logarithms are undefined for $x < 0$, -4 is an extraneous solution. The only solution is 2.

Exercises

Solve each equation. Check your solutions.

1. $\log_5 4 + \log_5 2x = \log_5 24$ **3**
2. $3 \log_4 6 - \log_4 8 = \log_4 x$ **27**
3. $\frac{1}{2} \log_6 25 + \log_6 x = \log_6 20$ **4**
4. $\log_2 4 - \log_2 (x + 3) = \log_2 8$ $-\dfrac{5}{2}$
5. $\log_6 2x - \log_6 3 = \log_6 (x - 1)$ **3**
6. $2 \log_4 (x + 1) = \log_4 (11 - x)$ **2**
7. $\log_2 x - 3 \log_2 5 = 2 \log_2 10$ **12,500**
8. $3 \log_2 x - 2 \log_2 5x = 2$ **100**
9. $\log_3 (c + 3) - \log_3 (4c - 1) = \log_3 5$ $\dfrac{8}{19}$
10. $\log_5 (x + 3) - \log_5 (2x - 1) = 2$ $2\dfrac{4}{7}$

NAME ___ DATE ___ PERIOD ___

8-5 Skills Practice

Properties of Logarithms

Use $\log_2 3 \approx 1.5850$ and $\log_2 5 \approx 2.3219$ to approximate the value of each expression.

1. $\log_2 25$ **4.6438**
2. $\log_2 27$ **4.755**
3. $\log_2 \frac{3}{5}$ **−0.7369**
4. $\log_2 \frac{5}{3}$ **0.7369**
5. $\log_2 15$ **3.9069**
6. $\log_2 45$ **5.4919**
7. $\log_2 75$ **6.2288**
8. $\log_2 0.6$ **−0.7369**
9. $\log_2 \frac{1}{3}$ **−1.5850**
10. $\log_2 \frac{9}{5}$ **0.8481**

Solve each equation. Check your solutions.

11. $\log_{10} 27 = 3 \log_{10} x$ **3**
12. $3 \log_7 4 = 2 \log_7 b$ **8**
13. $\log_4 5 + \log_4 x = \log_4 60$ **12**
14. $\log_6 2c + \log_6 8 = \log_6 80$ **5**
15. $\log_5 y - \log_5 8 = \log_5 1$ **8**
16. $\log_6 q - \log_6 3 = \log_6 7$ **21**
17. $\log_9 4 + 2 \log_9 5 = \log_9 w$ **100**
18. $3 \log_8 2 - \log_8 4 = \log_8 b$ **2**
19. $\log_{10} x + \log_{10} (3x - 5) = \log_{10} 2$ **2**
20. $\log_4 x + \log_4 (2x - 3) = \log_4 2$ **2**
21. $\log_3 d + \log_3 3 = 3$ **9**
22. $\log_{10} y - \log_{10} (2 - y) = 0$ **1**
23. $\log_2 r + 2 \log_2 5 = 0$ $\dfrac{1}{25}$
24. $\log_2 (x + 4) - \log_2 (x - 3) = 3$ **4**
25. $\log_4 (n + 1) - \log_4 (n - 2) = 1$ **3**
26. $\log_5 10 + \log_5 12 = 3 \log_5 2 + \log_5 a$ **15**

8-5 Practice
Properties of Logarithms

Use $\log_{10} 5 \approx 0.6990$ and $\log_{10} 7 \approx 0.8451$ to approximate the value of each expression.

1. $\log_{10} 35$ **1.5441**
2. $\log_{10} 25$ **1.3980**
3. $\log_{10} \frac{7}{5}$ **0.1461**
4. $\log_{10} \frac{5}{7}$ **−0.1461**
5. $\log_{10} 245$ **2.3892**
6. $\log_{10} 175$ **2.2431**
7. $\log_{10} 0.2$ **−0.6990**
8. $\log_{10} \frac{25}{7}$ **0.5529**

Solve each equation. Check your solutions.

9. $\log_7 n = \frac{2}{3}\log_7 8$ **4**
10. $\log_{10} u = \frac{3}{2}\log_{10} 4$ **8**
11. $\log_6 x + \log_6 9 = \log_6 54$ **6**
12. $\log_8 48 - \log_8 w = \log_8 4$ **12**
13. $\log_9 (3u + 14) - \log_9 5 = \log_9 2u$ **2**
14. $4\log_2 x + \log_2 5 = \log_2 405$ **3**
15. $\log_3 y = -\log_3 16 + \frac{1}{3}\log_3 64$ **$\frac{1}{4}$**
16. $\log_2 d = 5\log_2 2 - \log_2 8$ **4**
17. $\log_{10}(3m - 5) + \log_{10} m = \log_{10} 2$ **2**
18. $\log_{10}(b + 3) + \log_{10} b = \log_{10} 4$ **1**
19. $\log_8 (t + 10) - \log_8 (t - 1) = \log_8 12$ **2**
20. $\log_3 (a + 3) + \log_3 (a + 2) = \log_3 6$ **0**
21. $\log_{10}(r + 4) - \log_{10} r = \log_{10} (r + 1)$ **2**
22. $\log_4 (x^2 - 4) - \log_4 (x + 2) = \log_4 1$ **3**
23. $\log_{10} 4 + \log_{10} w = 2$ **25**
24. $\log_6 (n - 3) + \log_6 (n + 4) = 1$ **4**
25. $3\log_5 (x^2 + 9) - 6 = 0$ **±4**
26. $\log_{16}(9x + 5) - \log_{16}(x^2 - 1) = \frac{1}{2}$ **3**
27. $\log_6 (2x - 5) + 1 = \log_6 (7x + 10)$ **8**
28. $\log_2 (5y + 2) - 1 = \log_2 (1 - 2y)$ **0**
29. $\log_{10}(c^2 - 1) - 2 = \log_{10}(c + 1)$ **101**
30. $\log_7 x + 2\log_7 x - \log_7 3 = \log_7 72$ **6**

31. **SOUND** Recall that the loudness L of a sound in decibels is given by $L = 10\log_{10} R$, where R is the sound's relative intensity. If the intensity of a certain sound is tripled, by how many decibels does the sound increase? **about 4.8 dB**

32. **EARTHQUAKES** An earthquake rated at 3.5 on the Richter scale is felt by many people, and an earthquake rated at 4.5 may cause local damage. The Richter scale magnitude reading m is given by $m = \log_{10} x$, where x represents the amplitude of the seismic wave causing ground motion. How many times greater is the amplitude of an earthquake that measures 4.5 on the Richter scale than one that measures 3.5? **10 times**

8-5 Word Problem Practice
Properties of Logarithms

1. **MENTAL COMPUTATION** Jessica has memorized $\log_5 2 \approx 0.4307$ and $\log_5 3 \approx 0.6826$. Using this information, to the nearest thousandth, what power of 5 is equal to 6? **1.113**

2. **POWERS** A chemist is testing a soft drink. The pH of a solution is given by
$-\log_{10} C$,
where C is the concentration of hydrogen ions. The pH of a popular soft drink is 2.5. If the concentration of hydrogen ions is increased by a factor of 100, what is the new pH of the solution? **4.5**

3. **LUCKY MATH** Frank is solving a problem involving logarithms. He does everything correctly except for one thing. He mistakenly writes
$\log_2 a + \log_2 b = \log_2 (a + b)$.
However, after substituting the values for a and b in his problem, he amazingly still gets the right answer! The value of a was 11. What must the value of b have been? **1.1**

4. **LENGTHS** Charles has two poles. One pole has length equal to $\log_7 21$ and the other has length equal to $\log_7 25$. Express the length of both poles joined end to end as the logarithm of a single number. **$\log_7 525$**

5. **SIZE** Alicia wanted to try to quantify the terms *tiny, small, medium, large, big, huge,* and *humongous.* She picked a number of objects and classified them with these adjectives of size. She noticed that the scale seemed exponential. Therefore, she came up with the following definition. Define S to be $\frac{1}{3}\log_3 V$, where V is volume in cubic feet. Then use the following table to find the appropriate adjective.

S satisfies	Adjective
$-2 \le S < -1$	tiny
$-1 \le S < 0$	small
$0 \le S < 1$	medium
$1 \le S < 2$	large
$2 \le S < 3$	big
$3 \le S < 4$	huge
$4 \le S < 5$	humongous

a. Derive an expression for S applied to a cube in terms of ℓ where ℓ is the side length of a cube. **$\log_3 \ell$**

b. How many cubes, each one foot on a side, would have to be put together to get an object that Alicia would call "big"? **729**

c. How likely is it that a large object attached to a big object would result in a huge object, according to Alicia's scale? **Not very likely; most likely the result will be big, not huge.**

Answers (Lesson 8-5)

NAME _____ DATE _____ PERIOD _____

8-5 TI-Nspire Calculator Activity

Evaluating Logarithms

Logarithms can be evaluated on a TI-Nspire.

Example   Solve each equation to the nearest ten-thousandth.

a. $x = 2\log_3(7) - 3$

Enter the function into the calculator screen on the TI-Nspire.

Keystrokes: 2 ⎗ ⏷ 3 ▸ 7 ▸ ⏷ 3 ⏎

The solution to $x = 2\log_3(7) - 3$ is 0.5425.

b. $x = -7\log_{11}(196) + 3.3\log_7(247)$

Keystrokes: ⏷ 7 ⎗ ⏷ 11 ▸ 196 ▸ ⊕ 3.3 ⏷ ⎗ ⏷ 7 ▸ 247 ⏎

The solution of $x = -7\log_{11}(196) + 3.3\log_7(247)$ is -6.0648.

Exercises

Solve each equation to the nearest ten-thousandth.

1. $x = \log_3(87)$ **4.0650**

2. $x = \log_2(936)$ **9.8704**

3. $x = \log_{11}(19.84)$ **1.2460**

4. $\log_9(81)$ **2.0166**

5. $x = \log_6(451)$ **3.4109**

6. $x = \log_4(76)$ **3.1240**

7. $x = \log_7(54) + \log_4(23)$ **4.3117**

8. $x = \log_8(22) - \log_{13}(966)$ **-1.1932**

9. $x = 3\log_{14}(2) - 1.5$ **-0.7121**

10. $x = \log_4(12) - \log_{12}(4)$ **1.2346**

Chapter 8   39   *Glencoe Algebra 2*

NAME _____ DATE _____ PERIOD _____

8-5 Enrichment

Spirals

Consider an angle in standard position with its vertex at a point O called the pole. Its initial side is on a coordinatized axis called the *polar axis*. A point P on the terminal side of the angle is named by the *polar coordinates* (r, θ), where r is the directed distance of the point from O and θ is the measure of the angle. Graphs in this system may be drawn on polar coordinate paper such as the kind shown below.

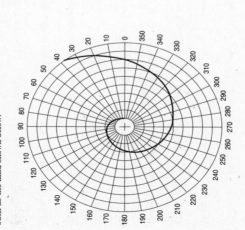

1. Use a calculator to complete the table for $\log_2 r = \dfrac{\theta}{120}$.

(*Hint:* To find θ on a calculator, press 120 × LOG) r) + LOG 2)).)

r	1	2	3	4	5	6	7	8
θ	0°	120°	190°	240°	279°	310°	337°	360°

2. Plot the points found in Exercise 1 on the grid above and connect to form a smooth curve.

This type of spiral is called a logarithmic spiral because the angle measures are proportional to the logarithms of the radii.

Chapter 8   38   *Glencoe Algebra 2*

NAME _____ DATE _____ PERIOD _____

8-6 Study Guide and Intervention

Common Logarithms

Common Logarithms Base 10 logarithms are called **common logarithms**. The expression $\log_{10} x$ is usually written without the subscript as $\log x$. Use the $\boxed{\text{LOG}}$ key on your calculator to evaluate common logarithms.

The relation between exponents and logarithms gives the following identity.

Inverse Property of Logarithms and Exponents | $10^{\log x} = x$

Example 1 Evaluate log 50 to the nearest ten-thousandth.

Use the $\boxed{\text{LOG}}$ key on your calculator. To four decimal places, $\log 50 = 1.6990$.

Example 2 Solve $3^{2x+1} = 12$.

$3^{2x+1} = 12$ Original equation
$\log 3^{2x+1} = \log 12$ Property of Equality for Logarithmic Functions.
$(2x+1)\log 3 = \log 12$ Power Property of Logarithms
$2x+1 = \dfrac{\log 12}{\log 3}$ Divide each side by log 3.
$2x = \dfrac{\log 12}{\log 3} - 1$ Subtract 1 from each side.
$x = \dfrac{1}{2}\left(\dfrac{\log 12}{\log 3} - 1\right)$ Multiply each side by $\frac{1}{2}$
$x = \dfrac{1}{2}\left(\dfrac{1.0792}{0.4771} - 1\right)$ Use a calculator.
$x \approx 0.6309$

Exercises

Use a calculator to evaluate each expression to the nearest ten-thousandth.

1. log 18   2. log 39   3. log 120
   1.2553   **1.5911**   **2.0792**

4. log 5.8   5. log 42.3   6. log 0.003
   0.7634   **1.6263**   **−2.5229**

Solve each equation or inequality. Round to the nearest ten-thousandth.

7. $4^{3x} = 12$ **0.5975**   8. $6^{x+2} = 18$ **−0.3869**

9. $5^{4x-2} = 120$ **1.2437**   10. $7^{3x-1} \geq 21$ $\{x \mid x \geq 0.8549\}$

11. $2 \cdot 4^{x+4} = 30$ **−0.1150**   12. $6.5^{2x} \geq 200$ $\{x \mid x \geq 1.4153\}$

13. $3.6^{4x-1} = 85.4$ **1.1180**   14. $2^{x+5} = 3^{x-2}$ **13.9666**

15. $9^{3x} = 4^{5x+2}$ **−8.1595**   16. $6^{x-5} = 2^{7x+3}$ **−3.6069**

Chapter 8   **40**   Glencoe Algebra 2

NAME _____ DATE _____ PERIOD _____

8-6 Study Guide and Intervention (continued)

Common Logarithms

Change of Base Formula The following formula is used to change expressions with different logarithmic bases to common logarithm expressions.

Change of Base Formula | For all positive numbers a, b, and n, where $a \neq 1$ and $b \neq 1$, $\log_a n = \dfrac{\log_b n}{\log_b a}$

Example Express $\log_8 15$ in terms of common logarithms. Then round to the nearest ten-thousandth.

$\log_8 15 = \dfrac{\log_{10} 15}{\log_{10} 8}$ Change of Base Formula
≈ 1.3023 Simplify.

The value of $\log_8 15$ is approximately 1.3023.

Exercises

Express each logarithm in terms of common logarithms. Then approximate its value to the nearest ten-thousandth.

1. $\log_3 16$ $\dfrac{\log 16}{\log 3}$, **2.5237**   2. $\log_2 40$ $\dfrac{\log 40}{\log 2}$, **5.3219**   3. $\log_5 35$ $\dfrac{\log 35}{\log 5}$, **2.2091**

4. $\log_4 22$ $\dfrac{\log 22}{\log 4}$, **2.2297**   5. $\log_{12} 200$ $\dfrac{\log 200}{\log 12}$, **2.1322**   6. $\log_2 50$ $\dfrac{\log 50}{\log 2}$, **5.6439**

7. $\log_5 0.4$ $\dfrac{\log 0.4}{\log 5}$, **−0.5693**   8. $\log_3 2$ $\dfrac{\log 2}{\log 3}$, **0.6309**   9. $\log_4 28.5$ $\dfrac{\log 28.5}{\log 4}$, **2.4164**

10. $\log_2 (20)^2$ $\dfrac{2\log 20}{\log 3}$, **5.4537**   11. $\log_6 (5)^4$ $\dfrac{4\log 5}{\log 6}$, **3.5930**   12. $\log_8 (4)^5$ $\dfrac{5\log 4}{\log 8}$, **3.3333**

13. $\log_5 (8)^3$ $\dfrac{3\log 8}{\log 5}$, **3.8761**   14. $\log_2 (3.6)^6$ $\dfrac{6\log 3.6}{\log 2}$, **11.0880**   15. $\log_{12} (10.5)^4$ $\dfrac{4\log 10.5}{\log 12}$, **3.7851**

16. $\log_3 \sqrt{150}$ $\dfrac{\log 150}{2\log 3}$, **2.2804**   17. $\log_4 \sqrt[3]{39}$ $\dfrac{\log 39}{3\log 4}$, **0.8809**   18. $\log_5 \sqrt[4]{1600}$ $\dfrac{\log 1600}{4\log 5}$, **1.1460**

Chapter 8   **41**   Glencoe Algebra 2

Chapter 8   **A19**   *Glencoe Algebra 2*

8-6 Practice

Common Logarithms

Use a calculator to evaluate each expression to the nearest ten-thousandth.

1. log 101 **2.0043**   2. log 2.2 **0.3424**   3. log 0.05 **−1.3010**

Use the formula $pH = -\log[H+]$ to find the pH of each substance given its concentration of hydrogen ions.

4. milk: $[H+] = 2.51 \times 10^{-7}$ mole per liter **6.6**

5. acid rain: $[H+] = 2.51 \times 10^{-6}$ mole per liter **5.6**

6. black coffee: $[H+] = 1.0 \times 10^{-5}$ mole per liter **5.0**

7. milk of magnesia: $[H+] = 3.16 \times 10^{-11}$ mole per liter **10.5**

Solve each equation or inequality. Round to the nearest ten-thousandth.

8. $2^x < 25$ **{x|x < 4.6439}**   9. $5^a = 120$ **2.9746**   10. $6^x = 45.6$ **2.1319**

11. $9^m \geq 100$ **{m|m ≥ 2.0959}** 12. $3.5^x = 47.9$ **3.0885**   13. $8.2^y = 64.5$ **1.9802**

14. $2^{b+1} \leq 7.31$ **{b|b ≤ 1.8699}**15. $4^{2x} = 27$ **1.1887**   16. $2^{n-4} = 82.1$ **10.3593**

17. $9^{a-2} > 38$ **{z|z > 3.6555}** 18. $5^{w+3} = 17$ **−1.2396**   19. $30^2 = 50$ **±1.0725**

20. $5^{x^2-3} = 72$ **±2.3785**   21. $4^{2x} = 9^{x+1}$ **3.8188**   22. $2^{x+1} = 5^{2x-1}$ **0.9117**

Express each logarithm in terms of common logarithms. Then approximate its value to the nearest ten-thousandth.

23. $\log_5 12$ $\dfrac{\log 12}{\log 5}$; **1.5440** 24. $\log_8 32$ $\dfrac{\log 32}{\log 8}$; **1.6667** 25. $\log_{11} 9$ $\dfrac{\log 9}{\log 11}$; **0.9163**

26. $\log_2 18$ $\dfrac{\log 18}{\log 2}$; **4.1699** 27. $\log_9 6$ $\dfrac{\log 6}{\log 9}$; **0.8155** 28. $\log_7 \sqrt{8}$ $\dfrac{\log 8}{2\log 7}$; **0.5343**

29. **HORTICULTURE** Siberian irises flourish when the concentration of hydrogen ions [H+] in the soil is not less than 1.58×10^{-8} mole per liter. What is the pH of the soil in which these irises will flourish? **7.8 or less**

30. **ACIDITY** The pH of vinegar is 2.9 and the pH of milk is 6.6. Approximately how many times greater is the hydrogen ion concentration of vinegar than of milk? **about 5000**

31. **BIOLOGY** There are initially 1000 bacteria in a culture. The number of bacteria doubles each hour. The number of bacteria N present after t hours is $N = 1000(2)^t$. How long will it take the culture to increase to 50,000 bacteria? **about 5.6 h**

32. **SOUND** An equation for loudness L in decibels is given by $L = 10 \log R$, where R is the sound's relative intensity. An air-raid siren can reach 150 decibels and jet engine noise can reach 120 decibels. How many times greater is the relative intensity of the air-raid siren than that of the jet engine noise? **1000**

8-6 Skills Practice

Common Logarithms

Use a calculator to evaluate each expression to the nearest ten-thousandth.

1. log 6 **0.7782**   2. log 15 **1.1761**

3. log 1.1 **0.0414**   4. log 0.3 **−0.5229**

Solve each equation or inequality. Round to the nearest ten-thousandth.

5. $3^x > 243$ **{x|x > 5}**   6. $16^v \leq \frac{1}{4}$ **{v|v ≤ −$\frac{1}{2}$}**

7. $8^x = 50$ **1.8813**   8. $7^x = 15$ **1.3917**

9. $5^{3b} = 106$ **0.9659**   10. $4^{5k} = 37$ **0.5209**

11. $12^{9p} = 120$ **0.2752**   12. $9^{2m} = 27$ **0.75**

13. $3^{x-5} = 4.1$ **6.2843**   14. $8^{y+4} > 15$ **{y|y > −2.6977}**

15. $7.6^{d+3} = 57.2$ **−1.0048**   16. $0.5^{x-8} = 16.3$ **3.9732**

17. $4.2^{x^2} = 84$ **±1.0888**   18. $5^{x^2+1} = 10$ **±0.6563**

Express each logarithm in terms of common logarithms. Then approximate its value to the nearest ten-thousandth.

19. $\log_3 7$ $\dfrac{\log 7}{\log 3}$; **1.7712**   20. $\log_5 66$ $\dfrac{\log 66}{\log 5}$; **2.6032**

21. $\log_2 35$ $\dfrac{\log 35}{\log 2}$; **5.1293**   22. $\log_6 10$ $\dfrac{\log 10}{\log 6}$; **1.2851**

23. Use the formula $pH = -\log[H+]$ to find the pH of each substance given its concentration of hydrogen ions.

a. gastric juices: $[H+] = 1.0 \times 10^{-1}$ mole per liter **1.0**

b. tomato juice: $[H+] = 7.94 \times 10^{-5}$ mole per liter **4.1**

c. blood: $[H+] = 3.98 \times 10^{-8}$ mole per liter **7.4**

d. toothpaste: $[H+] = 1.26 \times 10^{-10}$ mole per liter **9.9**

NAME _____ DATE _____ PERIOD _____

8-6 Enrichment

The Slide Rule

Before the invention of electronic calculators, computations were often performed on a slide rule. A slide rule is based on the idea of logarithms. It has two movable rods labeled with C and D scales. Each of the scales is logarithmic.

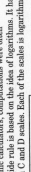

To multiply 2×3 on a slide rule, move the C rod to the right as shown below. You can find 2×3 by adding log 2 to log 3, and the slide rule adds the lengths for you. The distance you get is 0.778, or the logarithm of 6.

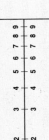

Follow the steps to make a slide rule. **1–2. See students' work.**

1. Use graph paper that has small squares, such as 10 squares to the inch. Using the scales shown at the right, plot the curve $y = \log x$ for $x = 1, 1.5$, and the whole numbers from 2 through 10. Make an obvious heavy dot for each point plotted.

2. You will need two strips of cardboard. A 5-by-7 index card, cut in half the long way, will work fine. Turn the graph you made in Exercise 1 sideways and use it to mark a logarithmic scale on each of the two strips. The figure shows the mark for 2 being drawn.

3. Explain how to use a slide rule to divide 8 by 2. **Line up the 2 on the C scale with the 8 on the D scale. The quotient is the number on the D scale below the 1 on the C scale.**

$y = \log x$

Chapter 8   45   *Glencoe Algebra 2*

NAME _____ DATE _____ PERIOD _____

8-6 Word Problem Practice

Common Logarithms

1. **OTHER BASES** Jamie needs to figure out what $\log_2 3$ is, but she only has a table of common logarithms. In the table, she finds that $\log_{10} 2 \approx 0.3010$ and $\log_{10} 3 \approx 0.4771$. Using this information, to the nearest thousandth, what is $\log_2 3$?
1.585

2. **pH** The pH of a solution is given by
$$-\log_{10} C,$$
where C is the concentration of hydrogen ions in moles per liter. A solution of baking soda creates a hydrogen ion concentration 5×10^{-9} of mole per liter. What is the pH of a solution of baking soda? Round your answer to the nearest tenth.
8.3

3. **GRAPHING** The graph of $y = \log_{10} x$ is shown below. Use the fact that
$$\frac{1}{\log_{10} 2} \approx 3.32$$
to sketch a graph of $y = \log_2 x$ on the same graph.

4. **SCIENTIFIC NOTATION** When a number n is written in scientific notation, it has the form $n = s \times 10^p$, where s is a number greater than or equal to 1 and less than 10 and p is an integer. Show that $p \le \log_{10} n < p + 1$.

$n = s \times 10^p$

$\log n = \log (s \times 10^p)$

$= \log s + \log 10^p$

$= \log s + p$

Because $1 \le s < 10$,

$0 \le \log s < 1$.

Therefore, $p \le \log n < p + 1$.

5. **LOG TABLE** Marjorie is looking through some old science books owned by her grandfather. At the back of one of them, there is a table of logarithms base 10. However, the book is worn out and some of the entries are unreadable.

Table of Common Logarithms (4 decimal places of accuracy)	
x	$\log_{10} x$
2	0.3010
3	0.4771
4	?
5	0.6989
6	?

a. Approximately what are the missing entries in the table? Round off your answers to the nearest thousandth.
$\log 4 \approx 0.602$
$\log 6 \approx 0.778$

b. How can you use this table to determine $\log_{10} 1.5$?
Sample answer: $\log 1.5$
$= \log 3 + \log 5 - \log 10$
$\approx 0.4771 + 0.6989 - 1$
≈ 0.1760

Chapter 8   44   *Glencoe Algebra 2*

8-6 TI-Nspire Calculator Activity

Common Logarithms

Common logarithms are graphed on a TI–Nspire as $\log_{10}$. (On some other graphing calculators, the LOG key is always defined for common logarithms.)

Example 1 Graph $y = 8 \log (x + 8)$.

Use the Graphs and Geometry function from the home menu to enter the equation.

Keystrokes: 62 8 10 8

The graph of $y = 8 \log(x + 8)$ is shown at the right.

Example 2 Estimate the coordinates of the intersection of $y = 8 \log (x + 8)$ and $y = 17 \log (x - 1)$ by graphing.

On the screen of $8 \log (x + 8)$, enter $17 \log (x - 1)$ on the $f2(x)$ line.

Keystrokes: 17 10 1

Now use the Intersection Point(s) command to find the intersection of the two lines.

Keystrokes: 63

Use the arrow keys to move the pointer to the first graph and click the center button. Then use the arrow keys to move the pointer to the second graph. Click, and the TI-Nspire will display the coordinates of the intersection on screen.

The intersection point of $y = 8 \log(x + 8)$ and $y = 17 \log(x - 1)$ is approximately (4.25, 8.71).

Exercises

Use a TI–Nspire to find the coordinates of the intersection of each pair of equations.

1. $y = 4 \log (3x + 2)$
$y = -3 \log (x - 4)$
(4.03, 4.60)

2. $y = 2 \log (2x)$
$y = 6 \log (x - 7)$
(9.69, 2.57)

3. $y = -3 \log (2x + 5)$
$y = -8 \log (x - 9)$
(12.59, −4.44)

4. $y = \frac{1}{3} \log(4x - 1)$
$y = -5 \log (3x - 1)$
(0.66, 0.07)

5. $y = x \log(x)$
$y = 0.4 \log(-22x + 270)$
(2.43, 0.93)

6. $y = -3 \log \left(\frac{5}{x}\right)$
$y = 2 \log (x^3)$
(0.2, −4.19)

Lesson 8-7

8-7 Study Guide and Intervention

Base e and Natural Logarithms

Base e and Natural Logarithms The irrational number $e \approx 2.71828...$ often occurs as the base for exponential and logarithmic functions that describe real-world phenomena.

Natural Base e	As n increases, $\left(1 + \frac{1}{n}\right)^n$ approaches $e \approx 2.71828...$.
	$\ln x = \log_e x$

The functions $f(x) = e^x$ and $f(x) = \ln x$ are inverse functions.

Inverse Property of Base e and Natural Logarithms	$e^{\ln x} = x$	$\ln e^x = x$

Natural base expressions can be evaluated using the e^x and $\ln$ keys on your calculator.

Example 1 Write a logarithmic equation equivalent to $e^{2x} = 7$.

$e^{2x} = 7 \rightarrow \log_e 7 = 2x$
$2x = \ln 7$

Example 2 Write each logarithmic equation in exponential form.

a. $\ln x \approx 0.3345$
$\ln x \approx 0.3345 \rightarrow \log_e x \approx 0.3345$
$x \approx e^{0.3345}$

b. $\ln 42 = x$
$\ln 42 = x \rightarrow \log_e 10 = x$
$10 = e^x$

Exercises

Write an equivalent exponential or logarithmic equation.

1. $e^{15} = x$
$\ln x = 15$

2. $e^{3x} = 45$
$3x = \ln 45$

3. $\ln 20 = x$
$e^x = 20$

4. $\ln x = 8$
$x = e^8$

5. $e^{-5x} = 0.2$
$-5x = \ln 0.2$

6. $\ln (4x) = 9.6$
$4x = e^{9.6}$

7. $e^{8.2} = 10x$
$\ln 10x = 8.2$

8. $\ln 0.0002 = x$
$e^x = 0.0002$

Evaluate each logarithm to the nearest ten–thousandth.

9. $\ln 12,492$
9.4328

10. $\ln 50.69$
3.9257

11. $\ln 9275$
9.1351

12. $\ln 0.835$
−0.1803

13. $\ln 943 - \ln 181$
1.6506

14. $\ln 67 + \ln 103$
8.8394

15. $\ln 931 \cdot \ln 32$
23.6927

16. $\ln (139 - 45)$
4.5433

Skills Practice

NAME _____ DATE _____ PERIOD _____

8-7 Skills Practice

Base e and Natural Logarithms

Write an equivalent exponential or logarithmic equation.

1. $e^x = 3$ $x = \ln 3$
2. $e^4 = 8x$ $4 = \ln 8x$

3. $\ln 15 = x$ $e^x = 15$

4. $\ln x \approx 0.6931$ $x \approx e^{0.6931}$

5. $e^4 = x - 3 \ln(x - 3) = 4$

6. $\ln 5.34 = 2x$ $5.34 = e^{2x}$

Write each as a single logarithm.

7. $3 \ln 3 - \ln 9$ $\ln 3$

8. $4 \ln 16 - \ln 256$ $2 \ln 16$

9. $2 \ln x + 2 \ln 4$ $\ln 16x^2$

10. $3 \ln 4 + 3 \ln 3$ $3 \ln 12$

Solve each equation or inequality. Round to the nearest ten-thousandth.

11. $e^x \geq 5$ $\{x | x \geq 1.6094\}$
12. $e^x < 3.2$ $\{x | x < 1.1632\}$

13. $2e^x - 1 = 11$ 1.7918

14. $5e^x + 3 = 18$ 1.0986

15. $e^{3x} = 30$ 1.1337
16. $e^{-4x} > 10$ $\{x | x < -0.5756\}$

17. $e^{8x} + 4 > 34$ $\{x | x > 0.6802\}$
18. $1 - 2e^{3x} = -19$ 1.1513

19. $\ln 3x = 2$ 2.4630
20. $\ln 8x = 3$ 2.5107

21. $\ln(x - 2) = 2$ 9.3891

22. $\ln(x + 3) = 1$ -0.2817

23. $\ln(x + 3) = 4$ 51.5982

24. $\ln x + \ln 2x = 2$ 1.9221

Chapter 8   49   *Glencoe Algebra 2*

Study Guide and Intervention

NAME _____ DATE _____ PERIOD _____

8-7 Study Guide and Intervention *(continued)*

Base e and Natural Logarithms

Equations and Inequalities with e and ln All properties of logarithms from earlier lessons can be used to solve equations and inequalities with natural logarithms.

Example Solve each equation or inequality.

a. $3e^{2x} + 2 = 10$

$3e^{2x} + 2 = 10$	Original equation
$3e^{2x} = 8$	Subtract 2 from each side.
$e^{2x} = \frac{8}{3}$	Divide each side by 3.
$\ln e^{2x} = \ln \frac{8}{3}$	Property of Equality for Logarithms
$2x = \ln \frac{8}{3}$	Inverse Property of Exponents and Logarithms
$x = \frac{1}{2} \ln \frac{8}{3}$	Multiply each side by $\frac{1}{2}$
$x \approx 0.4904$	Use a calculator.

b. $\ln(4x - 1) < 2$

$\ln(4x - 1) < 2$	Original inequality
$e^{\ln(4x - 1)} < e^2$	Write each side using exponents and base e.
$0 < 4x - 1 < e^2$	Inverse Property of Exponents and Logarithms
$1 < 4x < e^2 + 1$	Addition Property of Inequalities
$\frac{1}{4} < x < \frac{1}{4}(e^2 + 1)$	Multiplication Property of Inequalities
$0.25 < x < 2.0973$	Use a calculator.

Exercises

Solve each equation or inequality. Round to the nearest ten-thousandth.

1. $e^{4x} = 120$ 1.1969
2. $e^x \leq 25$ $\{x | x \leq 3.2189\}$
3. $e^{x-2} + 4 = 21$ 4.8332

4. $\ln 6x \geq 4$ $\{x | x \geq 9.0997\}$
5. $\ln(x + 3) - 5 = -2$ 17.0855
6. $e^{-8x} \leq 50$ $\{x | x \geq -0.4890\}$

7. $e^{4x-1} - 3 = 12$ 0.9270
8. $\ln(5x + 3) = 3.6$ 6.7196
9. $2e^{3x} + 5 = 2$ no solution

10. $6 + 3e^{x+1} = 21$ 0.6094
11. $\ln(2x - 5) = 8$ 1492.9790
12. $\ln 5x + \ln 3x > 9$ $\{x | x > 23.2423\}$

Chapter 8   48   *Glencoe Algebra 2*

Answers (Lesson 8-7)

NAME _____ DATE _____ PERIOD _____

8-7 Practice

Base e and Natural Logarithms

Write an equivalent exponential or logarithmic equation.

1. $\ln 50 = x$
$e^x = 50$

2. $\ln 36 = 2x$
$e^{2x} = 36$

3. $\ln 6 \approx 1.7918$
$e^{1.7918} \approx 6$

4. $\ln 9.3 \approx 2.2300$
$e^{2.2300} \approx 9.3$

5. $e^x = 8$
$x = \ln 8$

6. $e^5 = 10x$
$5 = \ln 10x$

7. $e^{-x} = 4$
$x = -\ln 4$

8. $e^2 = x + 1$
$2 = \ln (x + 1)$

Solve each equation or inequality. Round to four decimal places.

9. $e^x < 9$
$\{x | x < 2.1972\}$

10. $e^{-x} = 31$
-3.4340

11. $e^x = 1.1$
0.0953

12. $e^x = 5.8$
1.7579

13. $2e^x - 3 = 1$
0.6931

14. $5e^x + 1 \geq 7$
$\{x | x \geq 0.1823\}$

15. $4 + e^x = 19$
2.7081

16. $-3e^x + 10 < 8$
$\{x | x > -0.4055\}$

17. $e^{8x} = 8$
0.6931

18. $e^{-4x} = 5$
-0.4024

19. $e^{0.5x} = 6$
3.5835

20. $2e^{-5x} = 24$
0.4970

21. $e^{2x} + 1 = 55$
1.9945

22. $e^{3x} - 5 = 32$
1.2036

23. $9 + e^{2x} = 10$
0

24. $e^{-3x} + 7 \geq 15$
$\{x | x \leq -0.6931\}$

25. $\ln 4x = 3$
5.0214

26. $\ln (-2x) = 7$
-548.3166

27. $\ln 2.5x = 10$
8810.5863

28. $\ln (x - 6) = 1$
8.7183

29. $\ln (x + 2) = 3$
18.0855

30. $\ln (x + 3) = 5$
145.4132

31. $\ln 3x + \ln 2x = 9$
36.7493

32. $\ln 5x + \ln x = 7$
14.8097

33. INVESTING Sarita deposits $1000 in an account paying 3.4% annual interest compounded continuously. Use the formula for continuously compounded interest, $A = Pe^{rt}$, where P is the principal, r is the annual interest rate, and t is the time in years.

a. What is the balance in Sarita's account after 5 years? **$1185.30**

b. How long will it take the balance in Sarita's account to reach $2000? **about 20.4 yr**

34. RADIOACTIVE DECAY The amount of a radioactive substance y that remains after t years is given by the equation $y = ae^{kt}$, where a is the initial amount present and k is the decay constant for the radioactive substance. If $a = 100$, $y = 50$, and $k = -0.035$, find t. **about 19.8 yr**

NAME _____ DATE _____ PERIOD _____

8-7 Word Problem Practice

Base e and Natural Logarithms

1. INTEREST Horatio opens a bank account that pays 2.3% annual interest compounded continuously. He makes an initial deposit of 10,000. What will be the balance of the account in 10 years? Assume that he makes no additional deposits and no withdrawals.
$12,586

2. INTEREST Janie's bank pays 2.8% annual interest compounded continuously on savings accounts. She placed $2000 in the account. How long will it take for her initial deposit to double in value? Assume that she makes no additional deposits and no withdrawals. Round your answer to the nearest quarter year.
24.75 yr

3. BACTERIA A bacterial population grows exponentially, doubling every 72 hours.

bacteria	x	2x	4x	8x
time	0	72	144	216

Let P be the initial population size and let t be time in hours. Write a formula using the natural base exponential function that gives the size of the population as a function of P and t.
$P = e^{\frac{\ln 2}{72}t}$

4. POPULATION The equation $A = A_0 e^{rt}$ describes the growth of the world's population where A is the population at time t, A_0 is the population at time $t = 0$, and r is the annual growth rate. The world's population at the start of 2008 was estimated at 6,641,000,000. If the annual growth rate is 1.2%, when will the world population reach 9 billion?
2033

5. MONEY MANAGEMENT Linda wants to invest $20,000. She is looking at two possible accounts. Account A is a standard savings account that pays 3.4% annual interest compounded continuously. Account B would pay her a fixed amount of $200 every quarter.

a. If Linda can invest the money for 5 years only, which account would give her the higher return on her investment? How much more money would she make by choosing the higher paying account?
Account B; she'll make $24000 − $23706.10 = $293.90 more

b. If Linda can invest the money for 10 years only, which account would give her the higher return on her investment? How much more money would she make by choosing the higher paying account?
Account A; she'll make $28098.95 − $28000 = $98.95 more

c. If Linda can invest the money for 20 years only, which account would give her the higher return on her investment? How much more money would she make by choosing the higher paying account?
Account A; she'll make $39477.55 − $36000 = $3477.55 more

NAME _____ DATE _____ PERIOD _____

8-8 Study Guide and Intervention

Using Exponential and Logarithmic Functions

Exponential Growth and Decay

| Exponential Growth | $f(x) = ae^{kt}$ where a is the initial value of y, t is time in years, and k is a constant representing the rate of **continuous growth**. |
| Exponential Decay | $f(x) = ae^{-kt}$ where a is the initial value of y, t is time in years, and k is a constant representing the rate of **continuous decay**. |

Example POPULATION In 2000, the world population was estimated to be 6.124 billion people. In 2005, it was 6.515 billion.

a. Determine the value of k, the world's relative rate of growth

$$y = ae^{kt} \qquad \text{Formula for continuous growth.}$$
$$6.515 = 6.124e^{k(5)} \qquad y = 6.515,\ a = 6.124,\ \text{and } t = 2005 - 2000 = 5$$
$$\frac{6.515}{6.124} = e^{5k} \qquad \text{Divide each side by 6.124.}$$
$$\ln \frac{6.515}{6.124} = \ln e^{5k} \qquad \text{Property of Equality for Logarithmic Functions.}$$
$$\ln \frac{6.515}{6.124} = 5k \qquad \ln e^x = x$$
$$0.01238 = k \qquad \text{Divide each side by 5 and use a calculator.}$$

The world's relative rate of growth is about 0.01238 or 1.2%

b. When will the world's population reach 7.5 billion people?

$$7.5 = 6.124e^{0.01238t} \qquad y = 7.5,\ a = 6.124,\ \text{and } k = 0.01238$$
$$\frac{7.5}{6.124} = e^{0.01238t} \qquad \text{Divide each side by 6.124.}$$
$$\ln \frac{7.5}{6.124} = \ln e^{0.01238t} \qquad \text{Property of Equality for Logarithmic Functions.}$$
$$\ln \frac{7.5}{6.124} = 0.01238t \qquad \ln e^x = x$$
$$16.3722 = t \qquad \text{Divide each side by 0.01238 and use a calculator.}$$

The world's population will reach 7.5 billion in 2016

Exercises

1. **CARBON DATING** Use the formula $y = ae^{-0.00012t}$, where a is the initial amount of carbon 14, t is the number of years ago the animal lived, and y is the remaining amount after t years.

   a. How old is a fossil remain that has lost 95% of its Carbon-14?
   about 25,000 years old

   b. How old is a skeleton that has 95% of its Carbon-14 remaining?
   about 427 years old

NAME _____ DATE _____ PERIOD _____

8-7 Enrichment

Approximations for π and e

The following expression can be used to approximate e. If greater and greater values of n are used, the value of the expression approximates e more and more closely.

$$\left(1 + \frac{1}{n}\right)^n$$

Another way to approximate e is to use this infinite sum. The greater the value of n, the closer the approximation.

$$e = 1 + 1 + \frac{1}{2} + \frac{1}{2 \cdot 3} + \frac{1}{2 \cdot 3 \cdot 4} + \cdots + \frac{1}{2 \cdot 3 \cdot 4 \cdots n} + \cdots$$

In a similar manner, π can be approximated using an infinite product discovered by the English mathematician John Wallis (1616–1703).

$$\frac{\pi}{2} = \frac{2}{1} \cdot \frac{2}{3} \cdot \frac{4}{3} \cdot \frac{4}{5} \cdot \frac{6}{5} \cdot \frac{6}{7} \cdots \frac{2n}{2n-1} \cdot \frac{2n}{2n+1} \cdots$$

Solve each problem.

1. Use a calculator with an e^x key to find e to 7 decimal places. **2.7182818**

2. Use the expression $\left(1 + \frac{1}{n}\right)^n$ to approximate e to 3 decimal places. Use 5, 100, 500, and 7000 as values of n. **2.488, 2.705, 2.716, 2.718**

3. Use the infinite sum to approximate e to 3 decimal places. Use the whole numbers from 3 through 6 as values of n. **2.667, 2.708, 2.717, 2.718**

4. Which approximation method approaches the value of e more quickly? **the infinite sum**

5. Use a calculator with a π key to find π to 7 decimal places. **3.1415927**

6. Use the infinite product to approximate π to 3 decimal places. Use the whole numbers from 3 through 6 as values of n. **2.926, 2.972, 3.002, 3.023**

7. Does the infinite product give good approximations for π quickly? **no**

8. Show that $\pi^4 + \pi^5$ is equal to e^6 to 4 decimal places. **To 4 decimal places, they both equal 403.4288.**

9. Which is greater, e^π or π^e? **$e^\pi > \pi^e$**

10. The expression $x^{\frac{1}{x}}$ reaches a maximum value at $x = e$. Use this fact to prove the inequality you found in Exercise 9.
$$e^{\frac{1}{e}} > \pi^{\frac{1}{\pi}};\ \left(e^{\frac{1}{e}}\right)^{\pi e} > \left(\pi^{\frac{1}{\pi}}\right)^{\pi e};\ e^\pi > \pi^e$$

Answers (Lesson 8-8)

NAME _____ DATE _____ PERIOD _____

8-8 Skills Practice

Using Exponential and Logarithmic Functions

1. **FISHING** In an over-fished area, the catch of a certain fish is decreasing exponentially. Use $k = 0.084$ to determine how long will it take for the catch to reach half of its current the amount? **about 8.3 yr**

2. **POPULATION** A current census shows that the population of a city is 3.5 million. Using the formula $P = ae^{rt}$, find the expected population of the city in 30 years if the growth rate r of the population is 1.5%, a represents the current population in millions, and t represents the time in years. **about 5.5 million**

3. **POPULATION** The population P in thousands of a city can be modeled by the equation $P = 80e^{0.015t}$, where t is the time in years. In how many years will the population of the city be 120,000? **about 27 yr**

4. **BACTERIA** How many days will it take a culture of bacteria to increase from 2000 to 50,000? Use $k = 0.657$. **about 4.9 days**

5. **NUCLEAR POWER** The element plutonium-239 is highly radioactive. Nuclear reactors can produce and also use this element. The heat that plutonium-239 emits has helped to power equipment on the moon. If the half-life of plutonium-239 is 24,360 years, what is the value of k for this element? **about 0.00002845**

6. **DEPRECIATION** A Global Positioning Satellite (GPS) system uses satellite information to locate ground position. Abu's surveying firm bought a GPS system for $12,500. The GPS is now worth $8600. How long ago did Abu buy the GPS system? Use $k = 0.062$. **about 6.0 yr**

7. **LOGISTIC GROWTH** The population of a certain habitat follows the function.
$$p(t) = \frac{105,000}{1 + 2.7e^{-0.098t}}$$

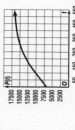

a. What is the maximum population of this habitat? **105,000**

b. When does the population reach 100,000? Round to the nearest hundredth. **t = 40.66**

NAME _____ DATE _____ PERIOD _____

8-8 Study Guide and Intervention (continued)

Using Exponential and Logarithmic Functions

Logistic Growth A logistic function models the S-curve of growth of some set λ. The initial stage of growth is approximately exponential; then, as saturation begins, the growth slows, and at some point, growth stops.

Example The population of a certain species of fish in a lake after t years is given by $P(t) = \dfrac{1880}{(1 + 1.42e^{-0.037t})}$.

a. Graph the function.

b. Find the horizontal asymptote.

The horizontal asymptote is $P(t) = 1880$.

c. What is the maximum population of the fish in the lake?

By looking at the graph we can tell that the population will reach a ceiling of 1880.

d. When will the population reach 1875?

Replace $P(t)$ by 1875 in the above equation: $1875 = \dfrac{1880}{(1 + 1.42e^{-0.037t})}$

Cross multiply: $1880 = 1875 \cdot (1 + 1.42e^{-0.037t})$

Divide by 1875 on both sides: $1.002667 = (1 + 1.42e^{-0.037t})$

$1.42e^{-0.037t} = -0.002667 \Rightarrow e^{-0.037t} = 0.00188779$

In both sides: $\ln(e^{-0.037t}) = \ln(0.00188779) \Rightarrow -0.037t = -6.277 \Rightarrow t = 169.66$ yr.

Exercises

1. Assume the population of a specific habitat follows the function: $P(t) = \dfrac{17000}{(1 + 15e^{-0.0082t})}$

a. Graph the function where $0 \le t \le 500$

b. What is the horizontal asymptote?
$y = 17,000$

c. What is the maximum population?
17,000

d. When does the population reach 15,000?
t = 132.987

8-8 Practice

Using Exponential and Logarithmic Functions

1. **BACTERIA** How many hours will it take a culture of bacteria to increase from 20 to 2000? Use $k = 0.614$. **about 7.5 hr**

2. **RADIOACTIVE DECAY** A radioactive substance has a half-life of 32 years. Find the constant k in the decay formula for the substance. **about 0.02166**

3. **RADIOACTIVE DECAY** Cobalt, an element used to make alloys, has several isotopes. One of these, cobalt 60, is radioactive and has a half-life of 5.7 years. Cobalt 60 is used to trace the path of nonradioactive substances in a system. What is the value of k for cobalt 60? **about 0.1216**

4. **WHALES** Modern whales appeared 5–10 million years ago. The vertebrae of a whale discovered by paleontologists contain roughly 0.25% as much carbon-14 as they would have contained when the whale was alive. How long ago did the whale die? Use $k = 0.00012$. **about 50,000 yr**

5. **POPULATION** The population of rabbits in an area is modeled by the growth equation $P(t) = 8e^{0.26t}$, where P is in thousands and t is in years. How long will it take for the population to reach 25,000? **about 4.4 yr**

6. **RADIOACTIVE DECAY** A radioactive element decays exponentially. The decay model is given by the formula $A = A_0 e^{-0.04463t}$. A is the amount present after t days and A_0 is the amount present initially. Assume you are starting with 50g. How much of the element remains after 10 days? 30 days? **about 32 g; about 13.1 g**

7. **POPULATION** A population is growing continuously at a rate of 3%. If the population is now 5 million, what will it be in 17 years' time? **about 8,326,455**

8. **BACTERIA** A certain bacteria is growing exponentially according to the model $y = 80e^{kt}$. Using $k = 0.071$, find how many hours it will take for the bacteria reach a population of 10,000 cells? **about 68 hr**

9. **LOGISTIC GROWTH** The population of a certain habitat follows the function:

$$P(t) = \frac{16,300}{(1 + 17.5e^{-0.065t})}$$

a. What is the maximum population? **16,300**

b. When does the population reach 16,200? $t = 122.3$

8-8 Word Problem Practice

Using Exponential and Logarithmic Functions

1. **PROGRAMMING** For reasons having to do with speed, a computer programmer wishes to model population size using a natural base exponential function. However, the programmer is told that the users of the program will be thinking in terms of the annual percentage increase. Let r be the percentage increase that the population increases each year. Find the value for k in terms of r so that
$e^k = 1 + r$.

$k = \ln(1 + r)$

2. **CARBON DATING** Archeologists uncover an ancient wooden tool. They analyze the tool and find that it has 22% as much carbon 14 compared to the likely amount that it contained when it was made. Given that the half-life of carbon 14 is about 5730 years, about how old is the artifact? Round your answer to the nearest 100 years.

12,500 yr

3. **POPULATION** The doubling time of a population is d years. The population size can be modeled by an exponential equation of the form Pe^{kt}, where P is the initial population size and t is time. What is k in terms of d?

$k = \dfrac{1}{d} \ln 2$

4. **POPULATION** Louisa read that the population of her town has increased steadily at a rate of 2% each year. Today, the population of her town has grown to 68,735.

Population	68,735	67,387	66,066	64,770
Year	Today	−1	−2	−3

Based on this information, what was the population of her town 100 years ago?

About 9,488 people.

5. **CONSUMER AWARENESS** Jason wants to buy a brand new high-definition (HD) television. He could buy one now because he has $7000 to spend, but he thinks that if he waits, the quality of HD televisions will improve. His $7000 earns 2.5% interest annually compounded continuously. The television he wants to buy costs $5000 now, but the cost increases each year by 7%.

a. Write a natural base exponential function that gives the value of Jason's account as a function of time t.
$7000e^{0.025t}$

b. Write a natural base exponential function that gives the cost of the television Jason wants as a function of time t.
$5000e^{(\ln 1.07)t}$

c. In how many years will the cost of the television exceed the value of the money in Jason's account? In other words, how much time does Jason have to decide whether he wants to buy the television? Round your answer to the nearest tenth of a year.

7.9 yr

6. **LOGISTIC GROWTH** The population of a bacteria, in thousands, can be modeled by $P(t) = \dfrac{22,000}{(1 + 1.2e^{-kt})}$ where t is time in hours and k is a constant.

a. After 1 hour the bacteria population is 10,532, what is the value of k?
0.0971

b. When does the population reach 21,900?
$t = 57.3$ hr

8-8 Spreadsheet Activity

Net Present Value

You have learned how to use exponential and logarithmic functions to perform a number of financial analyses. Spreadsheets can be used to perform many types of analyses, such as calculating the Net Present Value of expenditures or investments. For example, when a business owner is considering a major purchase, it is a good idea to find out whether the investment will be profitable in the future. Consider the example of a local restaurant-delivery service that is debating whether to buy a used van for $8000. The owners of the company estimate that the van will bring in $2500 per year over four years. They can use the following formula to find the present value of the future cash flow to find the Net Present Value (NPV), that is, how much the profits would be worth in today's dollars. NPV $= \frac{CF_n}{(1 + r)^n}$, where

CF_n = the cash flow in period n and r equals the cost of capital, which is either the interest that will be paid on a loan or the interest that the money would earn if it were invested.

◇	A	B	C
1	Cost of Asset	$8,000.00	
2	Cost of Capital (r)	0.1	
3			
4	Period (n)	CF	CF/(1+R)^n
5	1	$2,500.00	$2,272.73
6	2	$2,500.00	$2,066.12
7	3	$2,500.00	$1,878.29
8	4	$2,500.00	$1,707.53
9			$7,924.66
10			
11	Total		
12	NPV - Cost	−$75.34	

Sheet 1 / Sheet 2 / Sheet 3

Exercises

1. If the NPV is greater than the cost, the investment will pay for itself. Based on the spreadsheet shown above, would it be cost-effective for the company to buy the van? Explain. **The cost is actually about $75 greater than the NPV, so it would not be cost-effective to buy the van.**

2. Four times a year, Josey and Drew publish a magazine. They want to buy a color printer that costs $1750. The cost of capital for this purchase would be 6%. They are planning to raise the price of their magazine from $1 to $2. Create a spreadsheet to determine the NPV for this purchase.

   a. The last issue of the magazine sold 500 copies. If each issue of the magazine printed in color sells 100 copies more than the previous issue, is the printer a good investment after one year? Explain. **No, after one year the NPV is only about $1682.14.**

   b. If the sales of the magazine continue to rise at the same rate, is the printer a good investment after two years? **Yes, after two years the NPV is about $5210.28. The NPV is about $3460.28 greater than the cost.**

3. a. Calculate the NPV for an investment over a period of six years if the cost of capital is 4.5% and the investment will bring a cash flow of $750 every year. **The NPV would be about $3868.40.**

   b. Would this be a good investment of $3000? Explain? **Yes, the NPV is $1131.60 greater than the cost.**

8-8 Enrichment

Effective Annual Yield

When interest is compounded more than once per year, the effective annual yield is higher than the annual interest rate. The effective annual yield, E, is the interest rate that would give the same amount of interest if the interest were compounded once per year. If P dollars are invested for one year, the value of the investment at the end of the year is $A = P(1 + E)$. If P dollars are invested for one year at a nominal rate r compounded n times per year, the value of the investment at the end of the year is $A = P\left(1 + \frac{r}{n}\right)^n$. Setting the amounts equal and solving for E will produce a formula for the effective annual yield.

$P(1 + E) = P\left(1 + \frac{r}{n}\right)^n$

$1 + E = \left(1 + \frac{r}{n}\right)^n$

$E = \left(1 + \frac{r}{n}\right)^n - 1$

If compounding is continuous, the value of the investment at the end of one year is $A = Pe^r$. Again set the amounts equal and solve for E. A formula for the effective annual yield under continuous compounding is obtained.

$P(1 + E) = Pe^r$

$1 + E = e^r$

$E = e^r - 1$

Example 1 Find the effective annual yield of an investment made at 7.5% compounded monthly.

$r = 0.075$

$n = 12$

$E = \left(1 + \frac{0.075}{12}\right)^{12} - 1 \approx 7.76\%$

Example 2 Find the effective annual yield of an investment made at 6.25% compounded continuously.

$r = 0.0625$

$E = e^{0.0625} - 1 \approx 6.45\%$

Exercises

Find the effective annual yield for each investment.

1. 10% compounded quarterly **10.38%**
2. 8.5% compounded monthly **8.84%**
3. 9.25% compounded continuously **9.69%**
4. 7.75% compounded continuously **8.06%**
5. 6.5% compounded daily (assume a 365-day year) **6.72%**
6. Which investment yields more interest—9% compounded continuously or 9.2% compounded quarterly? **9.2% quarterly**

Chapter 8 Assessment Answer Key

Quiz 1 (Lessons 8-1 and 8-2)
Page 63

1.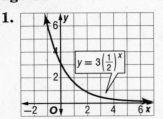

$y = 3\left(\frac{1}{2}\right)^x$

$D = \{$all real numbers$\}$
$R = \{y \mid y > 0\}$

2. $y = -5\left(\frac{1}{2}\right)^x$; decay

3. $-\dfrac{3}{2}$

4. $t \geq -1$

5. _____ B

Quiz 2 (Lessons 8-3 and 8-4)
Page 63

1. $\log_{81} 9 = \dfrac{1}{2}$

2. $216^{\frac{2}{3}} = 36$

3. $\dfrac{3}{2}$

4. $\dfrac{1}{4}$

5. $x \geq 1$

6. $\log_3 \left(\dfrac{1}{27}\right) = -3$

7. $\dfrac{9}{2}$

8. $\dfrac{5}{32}$

9. _____ 7

10. _____ C

Quiz 3 (Lessons 8-5 and 8-6)
Page 64

1. _____ 0.6095

2. _____ 1.9747

3. _____ C

4. _____ 1.7556

5. _____ 13.6972

Quiz 4 (Lessons 8-7 and 8-8)
Page 64

1. $3 = \ln 2x$

2. _____ 0.3

3. _____ 277.3 min

4. _____ C

5. $k \approx 0.0277$; $y = ae^{0.0277t}$

Mid-Chapter Test
Page 65

1. _____ C

2. _____ H

3. _____ B

4. _____ F

5. _____ A

6. _____ H

7. _____ A

8. _____ J

9. $y = -3(-2)^x$

10. $\left(\dfrac{1}{5}\right)^{-2} = m$

Answers

Chapter 8 Assessment Answer Key

Vocabulary Test
Page 66

1. natural logarithm

2. exponential function

3. exponential decay

4. natural logarithmic function

5. exponential growth

6. natural base exponential function

7. logarithmic function

8. exponential equations

9. common logarithm

10. growth factor

11. Sample answer:
    A logarithm is the power to which you must raise a number to get a specified number.

12. Sample answer:
    The natural base e is the base of natural logarithms. This is an irrational number that is approximately 2.71828.

Form 1
Page 67

1. B

2. J

3. A

4. F

5. C

6. J

7. B

8. F

9. D

10. H

Page 68

11. A

12. G

13. D

14. G

15. C

16. J

17. B

18. H

19. A

20. J

B: 21

Chapter 8 Assessment Answer Key

Form 2A
Page 69

1. B
2. J
3. C
4. J
5. C
6. J
7. B
8. J
9. C
10. F

Page 70

11. B
12. G
13. A
14. G
15. D
16. H
17. A
18. F
19. C
20. G

B: 4

Form 2B
Page 71

1. A
2. F
3. C
4. G
5. B
6. J
7. B
8. G
9. A
10. J

Page 72

11. C
12. H
13. A
14. G
15. C
16. F
17. B
18. J
19. B
20. F

B: 4

Answers

Chapter 8 Assessment Answer Key

1.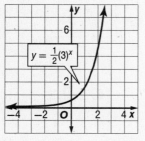

D = {all real numbers};
R = $\{y \mid y > 0\}$

2. decay

3. $y = -6\left(\dfrac{1}{3}\right)^x$

4. $x = -1$

5. -5

6. $\{x \mid x < 8\}$

7. $81^{-\frac{1}{2}} = \dfrac{1}{9}$

8. 7

9. $\dfrac{7}{2}$

10. 216

11. $\{x \mid x > 2\}$

12. 2.4054

13. 0.3174

14. 15

15. 1

16. 4

17. 4.1833

18. 3.5129

19. $\{x \mid x < 0.4679\}$

20. $\dfrac{\log 4}{\log 12} \approx 0.5579$

21. $\$3315.51$

22. 25.0855

23. $\{x \mid x \geq -0.5493\}$

24. $k \approx -0.0578;$
$y = ae^{-0.0578t}$

25. 17.4 yr

B: 9

Chapter 8 Assessment Answer Key

Form 2D
Page 75

1.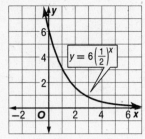

   D = {all real numbers};
   R = {y | y > 0}

2. growth

3. $y = -5\left(\frac{1}{2}\right)^x$

4. $x = 2$

5. 5

6. {x | x < 5}

7. $\log_5 \frac{1}{625} = -4$

8. 8

9. $\frac{7}{3}$

10. 16

11. {x | x ≥ 7}

12. 1.7959

13. 0.5693

Page 76

14. 28

15. $\frac{1}{4}$

16. 4

17. −0.7481

18. 5.1699

19. {x | x < 0.7783}

20. $\frac{\log 5}{\log 15} \approx 0.5943$

21. $610.70

22. 50.5982

23. {x | x ≥ −0.9635}

24. $k \approx -0.0575;$ $y = ae^{-0.0575t}$

25. 19.5 yr

B: 16

Answers

Chapter 8 Assessment Answer Key

Form 3
Page 77

Page 78

1.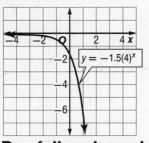

$D = \{\text{all real numbers}\};$
$R = \{y \mid y < 0\}$

2. decay

3. $y = -0.3(6)x$

4. $-\dfrac{1}{4}$

5. $\{m \mid m \le -4\}$

6. $8x - 1$

7. $5x$

8. 1

9. $\{a \mid a > 4\}$

10. 0.8212

11. 0.1133

12. 8

13. $-3, 8$

14. $\dfrac{x^3}{3}$

15. ± 0.5645

16. -5.4763

17. $\{t \mid t > 0.9958\}$

18. $\dfrac{3 \log 2.1}{\log 5} \approx 1.3830$

19. x^4

20. 1

21. $\{x \mid 0 < x < 2 \text{ or } x > 5\}$

22. $y = 663{,}906e^{-0.0038t}$

23. about 592,375 people

24. 4.7%

25. about 123 children

B: $100; 1$

Chapter 8 Assessment Answer Key

Score	General Description	Specific Criteria
4	**Superior** A correct solution that is supported by well-developed, accurate explanations	• Shows thorough understanding of the concepts of *graphing exponential functions, solving exponential and logarithmic equations and inequalities, using properties of logarithms and the Change of Base Formula, evaluating common and natural logarithms,* and *solving applied problems involving exponential growth and decay.* • Uses appropriate strategies to solve problems. • Computations are correct. • Written explanations are exemplary. • Goes beyond requirements of some of or all problems.
3	**Satisfactory** A generally correct solution, but may contain minor flaws in reasoning or computation	• Shows an understanding of most of the concepts of *graphing exponential functions, solving exponential and logarithmic equations and inequalities, using properties of logarithms and the Change of Base Formula, evaluating common and natural logarithms,* and *solving applied problems involving exponential growth and decay.* • Uses appropriate strategies to solve problems. • Computations are mostly correct. • Written explanations are effective. • Satisfies all requirements of problems.
2	**Nearly Satisfactory** A partially correct interpretation and/or solution to the problem	• *Shows an understanding of most of the concepts of graphing exponential functions, solving exponential and logarithmic equations and inequalities, using properties of logarithms and the Change of Base Formula, evaluating common and natural logarithms,* and *solving applied problems involving exponential growth and decay.* • May not use appropriate strategies to solve problems. • Computations are mostly correct. • Written explanations are satisfactory. • Satisfies the requirements of most of the problems.
1	**Nearly Unsatisfactory** A correct solution with no supporting evidence or explanation	• Final computation is correct. • No written explanations or work is shown to substantiate the final computation. • Satisfies minimal requirements of some of the problems.
0	**Unsatisfactory** An incorrect solution indicating no mathematical understanding of the concept or task, or no solution is given	• Shows little or no understanding of most of the concepts of *graphing exponential functions, solving exponential and logarithmic equations and inequalities, using properties of logarithms and the Change of Base Formula, evaluating common and natural logarithms,* and *solving applied problems involving exponential growth and decay.* • Does not use appropriate strategies to solve problems. • Computations are incorrect. • Written explanations are unsatisfactory. • Does not satisfy requirements of problems. • No answer may be given.

Answers

Chapter 8 Assessment Answer Key

Page 79, Extended-Response Test
Sample Answers

In addition to the scoring rubric found on page A35, the following sample answers may be used as guidance in evaluating open-ended assessment items.

1a. Sample answer: Choose $a = 2$, so $y = 2(1)^x$. All values for y are 2. Students should indicate that $y = a$ (regardless of their choice of a) is a constant function, not an exponential one, since the value of y never changes.

1b. Sample answer: Choose $a = 2$ and $b = -2$, so $y = 2(-2)^x$. The table of values for y are $-\frac{1}{4}, \frac{1}{2}, -1, 2, -4, 8,$ -16. Students should indicate that this function is not exponential. Since values of y alternate signs, the function does not continuously increase or decrease.

2a. Students should rewrite 9 as 3^2, then demonstrate the appropriate steps to show that $x = 4$.

2b. Students should take the common logarithm of both sides of the equation, then write all steps to

show that $x = \dfrac{6 \log 9}{5 \log 3 - \log 9}$ or 4.

2c. Sample answer: The first method is easier when both sides of an equation can be written as a power of the same base.

2d. Sample answer: $2^x = 16^{x+1}$; $x = -\dfrac{4}{3}$

3a. Sample answer: All three are logarithmic equations which can be written in exponential form as $(\text{base})^2 = x$. The bases of the three logarithms differ: the first equation has base 3, the second has base 10, and the third has base e.

3b. 9; 100; $e^2 \approx 7.3891$; Sample answer: $\log_5 x = 2$; 25

4a. Students should show all appropriate steps in reaching the final two steps:
$z(2 \log 2 - \log 12) \geq \log 12$

$z \geq \dfrac{\log 12}{2 \log 2 - \log 12} \approx -2.2619$

4b. Students should state that Ruby's checks show that her solution is incorrect.

4c. In the last step of her solution, Ruby should have changed the direction of the inequality symbol to obtain the solution $\{z \mid z \leq -2.2619\}$.

5a. Jones Corporation:
$10,000,000; \qquad $9,043,821
Davis Company:
$8,000,000; \qquad $8,836,977

5b. Students should indicate that since annual profits have been increasing for the Davis Company, stock in this company would most likely increase in value also.

5c. Students should demonstrate an understanding that the Jones Corporation's profit equation represents exponential decay since $b = 0.99$ (it is less than 1), while the Davis Company's profit equation represents exponential growth since $b = 1.01$ (it is greater than 1).

Chapter 8 Assessment Answer Key

Standardized Test Practice

Page 80

1. ● Ⓑ ⒸⒹ

2. ⒻⒼ ● Ⓙ

3. ⒶⒷⒸ ●

4. ⒻⒼⒽ ●

5. Ⓐ ● ⒸⒹ

6. ⒻⒼ ● Ⓙ

7. ● ⒷⒸⒹ

8. ⒻⒼ ● Ⓙ

9. ⒶⒷ ● Ⓓ

10. ⒻⒼⒽ ●

Page 81

11. ⒶⒷⒸ ●

12. ⒻⒼⒽ ●

13. ⒶⒷ ● Ⓓ

14. Ⓕ ● ⒽⒿ

15.

	1	0	8

16.

		4	8

Answers

Chapter 8 Assessment Answer Key

Standardized Test Practice
Page 82

17. **between 0 and −1; 1**

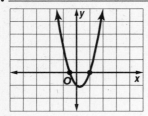

18. $x^2 + 4x - 16; x^2 - 14; 2x^3 + 3x^2 - 32x + 15; \dfrac{x^2 + 2x - 15}{2x - 1}, x \neq \dfrac{1}{2}$

19. $\dfrac{2p^2r^4}{5m}$

20. $\dfrac{7}{x - 5}$

21. $y = 4\left(\dfrac{1}{5}\right)^x$

22a. $t \geq 0, r \geq 0,$
$t + r \leq 90,$
$25t + 40r \leq 3000;$
$(0, 0), (0, 75),$
$(40, 50), (90, 0)$

22b. $f(t, r) = 14t + 20r$

22c. **40 tent sites, 50 RV sites; $1560**

ARRL MEMBERS

This proof of purchase may be used as a $1.20 credit on your next ARRL purchase. Limit one coupon per new membership, renewal or publication ordered from ARRL Headquarters. No other coupon may be used with this coupon. Validate by entering your membership number from your *QST* label below:

From _____

_____

_____

EDITOR, NEW HAM COMPANION
AMERICAN RADIO RELAY LEAGUE
225 MAIN STREET
NEWINGTON CT 06111-1494

— — — — — — — — — — — — — — — — please fold and tape — — — — — — — — — — — — — — — —

F E E D B A C K

Please use this form to give us your comments on this book and what you'd like to see in future editions, or e-mail us at **pubsfdbk@arrl.org** (publications feedback).

Where did you purchase this book?
□ From ARRL directly   □ From an ARRL dealer

Is there a dealer who carries ARRL publications within:
□ 5 miles   □ 15 miles   □ 30 miles of your location?   □ Not sure.

License class:
□ Novice   □ Technician   □ Technician Plus   □ General   □ Advanced   □ Amateur Extra

Name _____   ARRL member? □ Yes □ No

Call Sign _____

Daytime Phone ( ) _____   Age _____

Address _____

City, State/Province, ZIP/Postal Code _____

Licensed, how long? _____

Other hobbies _____

Occupation _____

this phenomenon. Voltage depression is probably the most likely culprit in most cases (see Figure 2).

While it's even possible for a cell loss of only one-tenth of a volt to go unnoticed, perhaps the best news of all is this: *Even if you experience memory effect, it's neither permanent nor fatal.* One or two complete charge/discharge cycles is all it takes to restore your NiCd to original condition. (I am defining a "complete discharge" in this case as 1.0 V per cell. You'll find out why later.)

The NiCds in My Home and Shack

I've had good luck with my NiCds. In fact, the current champions around our house are the batteries in my cordless electric razor. They've seen daily use for almost 10 years now and they're still going strong! The following guidelines have worked well for me and represent my personal philosophy on the treatment of NiCd batteries:

☐ First and foremost, I always follow the manufacturer's instructions for any given product. The one exception I make, however, is never to intentionally discharge my NiCds until they are completely depleted. As I indicated previously, my rule of thumb is never to discharge a NiCd cell to less than 1.0 V. Discharging cells beyond this limit can lead to cell reversal and shortened battery life. See Figure 3 for a description of cell reversal.

But what if you can't conveniently measure the cell voltages? A typical example is the electric toothbrush that my wife recently purchased. It came with instructions to initially charge the batteries, but not to recharge them until they are depleted. The manual also recommends a complete discharge once a year or so. While I may leave the charger unplugged for a few days at these times, I'll be sure to reconnect it before the NiCds are completely dead.

☐ Second, in the absence of instructions to the contrary, I only recharge when convenient or necessary. I find the normal variations of the charge/discharge regime of most appliances to be more than adequate to prevent the onset of memory effect. (And yes, I do occasionally forget to start recharging an appliance before the batteries run out!) I also use this as a guideline for appliances that have automatic shut-down at a predetermined voltage level, but I admit to having only minimal experience with such devices.

☐ And third, only if I suspect or encounter memory effects do I intentionally discharge my batteries to the 1.0 V level. Remember, this effect is neither permanent nor fatal. Why subject NiCds to unnecessary and life-shortening stress, especially when such a simple procedure will reverse it?

Discharge Before Charge

You may have seen NiCd chargers that have a discharge-before-charge feature. These devices enable you to conveniently discharge NiCds to a predetermined level before charging them. Although I do not recommend using a discharge feature to prevent the onset of memory effect (only as a last resort, if you suspect memory effect), the discharge feature can help correct NiCd *cell imbalance.* This problem occurs when multiple cells connected in series have unequal charges.

Imbalance can be promoted by the use of a *peak*-type full-charge detector (see Figure 4). If some, but not all, of the cells achieve full capacity during a charge cycle, a voltage peak can still be generated. This peak tricks the charger into shutting off, even though some cells are not yet at full charge. Cell imbalance is a rather common problem with NiCds—far more common than memory effect.

To properly balance NiCds, first discharge and recharge them in the normal fashion. Then, once the initial charge is complete, continue to trickle charge your battery until you are certain all cells are at full charge.

Another problem associated with fast chargers is overcharging. If a fast charger fails to detect that full capacity on even a single cell has been reached, charging continues and cell *outgassing* can occur. Loss of cell capacity always accompanies cell outgassing.

You can find more about NiCds and the memory effect by reading "Getting the Most Out Of Nickel-Cadmium Batteries" by Ken Stuart, W3VVN, in February 1992 *QST* and "A Microcomputer-Controlled NiCd Battery Charger" by Tim Ahrens, WA5VQR, in August 1990 *QST.* Two other good sources of information are: *Maintenance-Free Batteries,* by D. Berndt, published by John Wiley & Sons, and *Rechargeable Batteries Applications Handbook,* by the Technical Marketing Staff of Gates Energy Products Inc, published by Butterworth-Heinemann, a division of Reed Publishing.

Many thanks to ARRL Technical Advisor Ken Stuart, W3VVN, for his assistance during the preparation of this article.

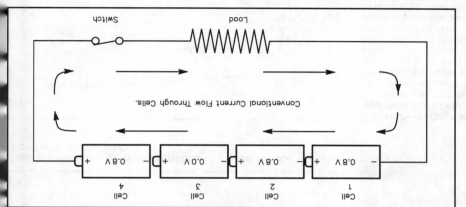

Figure 3—NiCd battery packs should not be discharged to a level less than 1.0 V per cell. Overdischarging a series-connected battery pack can lead to cell reversal—a phenomenon detrimental to NiCd longevity. During overdischarge, differences in individual cell capacity can lead to one cell becoming depleted before the others. In the example shown, cell 3 is completely discharged, while cells 1, 2 and 4 are still at 0.8 V. At this point, the current generated by the remaining active cells will "charge" cell 3, *but in reverse polarity.* Cell reversal can lead to outgassing and permanent damage to NiCds. If you accidentally overdischarge your NiCds and experience a cell reversal, try recharging the pack for the full time recommended by the manufacturer. One or two occurrences of cell reversal probably won't destroy the pack, but try not to let it happen again.

Switch — Load — Conventional Current Flow Through Cells. — Cell 1 0.8 V — Cell 2 0.8 V — Cell 3 0.0 V — Cell 4 0.8 V

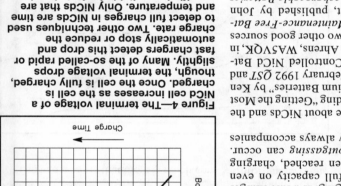
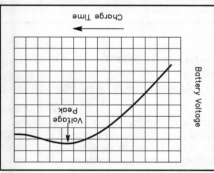

Battery Voltage — Voltage Peak — Charge Time

Figure 4—The terminal voltage of a NiCd cell increases as the cell is charged. Once the cell is fully charged, though, the terminal voltage drops slightly. Many of the so-called rapid or fast chargers detect this drop and automatically stop or reduce the charge rate. Two other techniques used to detect full charges in NiCds are time and temperature. Only NiCds that are specified as suitable for fast charging should be used in this type of charger.

A NiCd Never Forgets.
Or Does It?

A lot of folklore has accumulated about memory effect and nickel-cadmium (NiCd) rechargeable batteries.
It's time to separate myth from fact.

By Mike Gruber, WA1SVF
ARRL Laboratory Engineer

When the conversation drifts to rechargeable batteries—NiCds in particular—someone is sure to bring up the dreaded *memory effect*. True memory effect refers to a specific type of deterioration in NiCd cell performance. It manifests itself as a reduction in cell voltage, usually in the order of a few tenths of a volt, and is brought on by many repeated shallow charge/discharge cycles (see Figure 1).

First, the Bad News about Memory Effect

The bad news is that there is much con-troversy surrounding the memory effect, despite decades of NiCd use in industrial and consumer products. Much of the debate surrounds the procedure of dis-charging NiCds before charging. Propo-nents argue that discharging is necessary to prevent memory effect, while opponents claim that it's just a waste of valuable cell life. (NiCds typically enjoy a life-span of about 200 complete charge/discharge cycles. More cycles are possible with less than a complete discharge.) Some dis-miss both extremes and advocate an occasional discharge before charge. Unfortunately, the frequency of the pro-cedure is still a subject of debate.

Now for the Good News

The good news is that the preponder-ance of evidence suggests true memory effect is very rare. It usually takes many shallow discharge cycles to *precisely* the same discharge point before memory effect occurs. (Conditions such as these were present in communications satellites, where memory effect was first observed.) Some battery manufacturers even claim their batteries exhibit no memory effect at all. For this reason, I suspect other types of battery problems are often mistaken for

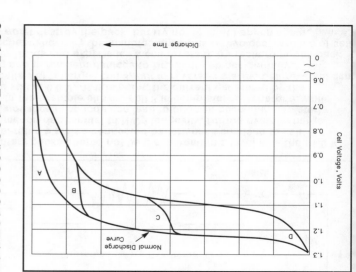

Figure 1—Discharge characteristics of a normal NiCd versus a cell with memory effect.

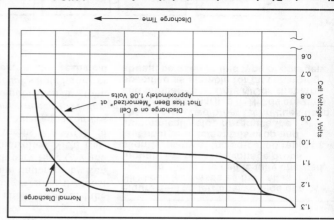

voltage depression. It's best, however, to prevent voltage depression from occurring in the first place by not overcharging your NiCds.

Figure 2—Voltage depression symptoms closely mimic the true memory effect. So much so, in fact, some people tend to define voltage depression and true memory effect as one phenomenon called "memory." The two, however, are quite different. Be sure to understand which of these effects, as well as any others, are considered as "memory" when you encounter other discussions on this topic. Voltage depression in NiCds is caused by long, continuous overcharging. The effect is initially limited at the end of the discharge cycle as indicated by curve B. As the length of overcharge time increases, the effect starts occurring sooner during the discharge period, such as illustrated by curve C. If the overcharge is severe enough, the discharge curve takes on the shape produced by a normal cell, but the whole curve is depressed, as shown by curve D. Voltage depression is caused by the growth of crystals inside the battery. These crystals in turn cause an increase in the battery's internal resistance. Fortunately, like the true memory effect, this is a reversible phenomenon. One or more deep discharge/charge cycles is all it takes to reverse